# 17

# *Again*

### *a story of*
# LIFE AFTER LIFE

# 17 Again

## a story of
## LIFE AFTER LIFE

## LISA BOULLT

IDUN

NASHVILLE, TENNESSEE

Note: This is a work of fiction based on true events and is a compilation of the author's recollection of these events. Some names, people, places, and incidents have been changed for privacy. Locales and public names are sometimes used for atmospheric purposes.

Idun is an imprint of W. Brand Publishing

Permission information: j.brand@wbrandpub.com

www.wbrandpub.com


Cover design by designchik.net

*17 Again* / Lisa Boullt—first edition


Available in Hardcover, Paperback, Kindle, and eBook formats.

Hardcover ISBN:  978-1-956906-63-9

Paperback ISBN: 978-1-956906-62-2

eBook ISBN: 978-1-956906-64-6

Library of Congress Control Number: 2023912759

# CONTENTS

*This book is dedicated to and in loving memory of my sister, Andrea, and my parents, Judy and Billy.*

*This story takes place in Monroe, Louisiana, from 1976-1993, a time much different from today. There were no cell phones, internet, YouTube, Facebook, or any social media. Author Lisa Boullt guides the reader in Andrea's voice through her journey of life after life, sharing the importance of organ donation, friendship, and hope and love.*

# CHAPTER 1

# *This is Us*

*L*et me introduce myself. My name is Andrea Michelle Boullt. I was born on August 10th, 1976, in Monroe, Louisiana in the Northeast part of the state, also known as Bayou country.

In 1993, I turned seventeen and was ready to take on the world, or so I thought. Life as I knew it changed forever on November 7th of that year.

The youngest of three children, I was the baby of the family, affectionate and completely irresistible with curly, long blond hair and crystal blue eyes. My brother Jerry was the oldest, fourteen years older than me. Lisa was in the middle and seven years older. We couldn't have been more different, yet so alike. They were the best big brother and sister anyone could ask for.

Some called us the perfect family because, on the outside, it appeared we were, but rarely nothing was as it seemed. We had our share of problems like any other family, but we made the best out of any situation.

My parents, Billy and Judy, were married for almost twenty-five years until they divorced in December 1992. They had been through many hard times years earlier and worked through it until they drifted apart again. That was when things started changing in my world. My family wasn't together anymore.

In my short seventeen years, our family had been through a lot of good and some not-so-good moments. I was grateful enough to have some of the best friends a girl could ask for, who helped me get through some of those hard times. My true friendships were far and few between, but I always had tons of friends around. I learned at an early age that true friendships can feel like family.

Hold on, I'm getting way ahead of myself. Let me tell you a little bit about my childhood and how things were growing up for my siblings and me.

We were all born in the downtown district of Monroe, Louisiana, at the same hospital, St. Francis Medical Center.

Louisiana is ranked the third lowest and flattest state, but it's also pretty fascinating. We never had four seasons like most parts of the country unless it was all in one day, which sometimes happened. We mainly had two seasons, summer and winter.

Winters were short and mild, with rarely any snow, mostly freezing rain or sleet, but it would get pretty cold. I remember a few times there was enough snow to make a snowman. Mom had a picture of us all bundled up with a tiny snowman with one of Jerry's hats and Dad's necktie on.

Summers were usually wetter than the rest of the year and really hot and humid, which if you know, wasn't the best for curly hair. On those days, my hair ended up in a ponytail and looked like a cotton ball on my head, but I didn't care. Mom kept a ponytail holder in her purse just for those moments. Lisa didn't have to worry about it because her hair was straight as a board and didn't get curly till she became a teenager.

Monroe was known as the hottest city in the state, with the highest recorded temperatures. I mean, sometimes it would get over 100 degrees with an even higher heat index. So, on those days, we would crank up the AC and get our box fans out to cool the house off. It would be hard to have a conversation if the fans were on because they were so loud, but it didn't matter because it helped keep the house cool.

What Louisiana lacked in official seasons is made up for with its own: Mardi Gras, Pollen, Hurricane, and one of the most popular, Crawfish Season. Our state had been called the Crawfish capital of the world. Crawfish season is a big deal in Monroe. March till June is the best time to get the bigger crawfish, but you can still get them later though they are smaller.

Crawfish boils were fun events to go to, where huge pots were filled with crawfish, corn, and potatoes. It all soaked up the spices, and it could get really spicy too. Peeling a crawfish took practice, though it always seemed like a lot of work to me just to get a little piece of meat.

Louisiana, known for its delicious food, music scene, cotton fields, and many historical landmarks, makes the Bayou state special. However, I would say the food was top of that list. Some of the most popular dishes in north Louisiana are different from south Louisiana.

If you visited north Louisiana, you might be served catfish, purple hulled peas, cornbread, any kind of barbeque with a side of cabbage or collard greens, and pecan pie for dessert. In south Louisiana, the food was different, with more Creole and Cajun cuisine. Dishes like Gumbo, Jambalaya, Crawfish etouffee, dirty rice, and beignets. Southern cuisine could be on the spicy side.

We were always surrounded by food, from tailgating before a big football game to weddings, funerals, and graduations. Everything revolved around what we were going to eat.

Monroe, the largest city in Northeast Louisiana and my hometown, is located about 115 miles west of the Mississippi River along Interstate 20. This part of Louisiana is known as Sportsman's Paradise.

There was always something to do outdoors, usually around water and woods: hunting, fishing, water skiing, swamp tours down south, museum tours, hiking. One of my favorite things to do was go to Chennault Park. We would go there on weekends and spend the day. There were pavilions where we could cook out and have a picnic. The biggest water slide I had ever seen, called Critters Creek, was inside the park; it was made from cement and rough on your bottom and legs, so you had to make sure to stay on the mats going down. Across the river was West Monroe, about half the size of Monroe, which was also referred to as the Twin Cities.

My Mom and Dad met in a bar in November of 1966, or so we had always been told. They got married a year later by a justice of the peace on a Thursday night in August of 1967. They didn't have a big wedding or even pictures from their wedding day. Dad's sister, Betty, and her future husband, NJ, were their witnesses. No one else knew they were getting married. They just showed up married at Betty and NJ's wedding the next day. Everyone was surprised, including their parents.

My Mom had my brother, Jerry, when she was younger and had been married to his dad for a brief time before she and Jerry moved back in with her parents in Lakeshore, which was outside of Monroe city limits. After she and Dad met, fell in love, and married, they started our family. My sister, Lisa, was born in 1969, and I was born in 1976.

We lived in a little white house on Crescent Drive on the south side of town. It wasn't really large enough for a family of five, but we didn't know anything different. It was around 1200 square feet with only one full bathroom and a half-bath in my parents' room. The previous owners closed in the carport and made it an extra living space where we would play.

Lisa started taking piano lessons the same year I was born; her teacher Miss Magoo lived right down the street so she could ride her bicycle to her lessons once a week. After Lisa realized she was serious about playing piano, Mom and Dad bought a brown upright piano for Lisa that was placed in the living room at the front of the house.

Lisa had her own room until I came along, and that's when we started sharing a room. My baby bed was in the left corner next to the toy box. Jerry had his own room right next to ours, and Mom and Dad were across the hall. Because I was so young when we lived there, I don't remember much about that house, but seeing pictures reminded me it was special. Lisa and Jerry had more memories of living there since they spent most of their early years there.

Mom and Dad were raised Catholic, so they decided to raise us in the Catholic religion. We went to St. Joseph

Catholic Church early on, where all three of us were baptized and had our first communion. Jerry went to Our Lady of Fatima Catholic School until the fourth grade, Minnie Ruffin for middle school, and Ouachita for junior and high school. Lisa was next in line to go to Fatima and start the fourth grade; she had her uniforms ready to go, but then we moved, and they started going to public schools. Lisa at Jack Hayes and Jerry at Ouachita, but we made Our Lady of Fatima our family church because it was closer to our new home.

My Mom had worked at the Little Red School House since Lisa was a baby. It was the perfect job for a Mom with young kids. She could bring us to work with her; it was free for employees. Jerry never went there since he was already in school. Lisa started there at a year old, through kindergarten, and then went to the private school until she was in third grade that Little Red School House created. No more than ten kids were in her class in first through third grade. I started going with Mom right after she came back from maternity leave. So, I basically grew up there. Jerry would only go to Little Red School House in the summers and take swimming lessons when he was younger.

My family moved to the north side of town in 1980 when I was three. Mom first worked at the West Monroe Little Red School House until they opened a new location in the town's Town and Country area. They offered Mom the opportunity to take on a management position.

Mom and Dad had always wanted to live on the north side of town, which was closer to the daycare, so it was the perfect opportunity to make a change. We moved to the home I was raised in. My Dad worked for Hostess, so it didn't matter where he lived since his truck route was all over the area.

They bought a bigger ranch-style house in a neighborhood called Treasure Island right off 165 north of town. It was about 1650 square feet which felt much bigger, and we had two full bathrooms, which definitely made a difference. Our main bathroom was in the hallway all of us kids shared, and Mom and Dad had another full bath in their master bedroom.

The walls were dark brown paneling throughout the house in most rooms. Our most recent school pictures hung on the walls down the hall. Mom and Dad loved pictures, which must have influenced us, I guess. The double exposure portraits were a popular trend then. It was weird how they did it, but they took a front picture and a side view and superimposed them on the same photo; it was the style back then. Lisa hated hers, but Mom and Dad hung it proudly in the hallway along with mine and Jerry's.

Our ranch-style house had a formal living room which we never used, a den where everyone gathered, and a dining room used on special holidays and family dinner nights. We mostly ate at the bar but sat in the dining room when the whole family was together.

The piano was in the formal living room, giving us a little more privacy when we practiced. The den is where we spent most of our family time. Our furniture was brown and gold plaid with a matching chair and ottoman. Dad had a light brown leather recliner in the corner where he would watch TV, which meant "nap" most of the time.

A set of *World Book Encyclopedias* lined a brown shelf near the TV in the den. The twenty-two book collection was alphabetized from A-Z by subject matter, which made researching easier, and were off-white with gold trim paper. We would use these if we didn't go to the library to research for a school project. Information was constantly changing, so the books became outdated quickly. They released a new edition every year, but we didn't get them. I played with them, and not knowing the order, they would usually stay mixed up, but that's how I learned the alphabet.

Home interior decorating became a popular thing. Mom had friends from work who sold décor for the home as a part-time job, and they would host parties to show off their pieces and sell them. It was also a way for friends to get together and catch up. Most houses in the '70s and '80s had some of the same pieces hanging on the wall.

I remembered one picture she got, called Rustic Autumn Farm, hung on one wall and a scary owl picture with matching gold sconces on each side. We had owl paintings all through the house. I'm not sure why the owls were so popular back then; they kind of creeped me out since it looked like they were always staring at me. Mom also found little statues that went on the piano of a boy playing a horn and a girl holding her ears. Those pieces stayed with the piano through the years.

Our neighborhood, Treasure Island ,was a fun place to live; there was only one way in and out. It was named after the book because it was an actual island; surrounded by the Black Bayou, which looked black with the trees covered in moss hanging almost to the water. The houses on the Bayou side had beautiful views with docks in the backyards and sometimes an alligator or two. Anyone with small dogs had to be careful and not let them roam. The street names all had a nautical theme, like Captain Hook, Pirate, Silver, Spyglass, and our street, Jolly Roger. We lived almost in the direct center of the island. This ranch-style house would be the only home I would ever know. Many memories were made on that corner lot at the end of the street at 109 Jolly Roger Drive.

I grew up in a time with no smartphones or computers. We communicated through actual letters or snail mail, our home telephone, or just by going to a friend's house to see if they were home. You could usually tell where everyone hung out by the number of bicycles in front of the house. After school, we would come home and change into our play clothes so we didn't ruin our school clothes. This made more laundry for us to do, but it also kept us from messing up the clothes we wore to church and school.

Our kitchen wasn't very large, so we would sit at the bar and talk when Mom or Dad were cooking. An avocado green rotary dial telephone was mounted to the wall by the bar with a long spiral cord that stretched across the room. The bar was gold colored with wooden barstools that we sat in when we were on a call. The phone cord was sturdy, so if we needed to step into the laundry room for some privacy, we could shut the door without breaking the cord. Each of our bedrooms had its own phone, too, that shared the same line.

We never really had much privacy on calls, though. Most of the time, I would pick up when Lisa was on the phone to listen in to her friends talking about the cute boys at school. Lisa could tell when I picked up because I would be giggling on the other end, trying hard to stay quiet, which was almost impossible for me.

The new house had three bedrooms, meaning Lisa and I still had to share a room. Our parents bought us matching twin beds when we moved into the new house. They were off-white with gold color trim, and the dresser and desk with a matching hutch to complete the set.

For entertainment, we had a main color TV in the den where the family gathered; it had only a few local channels until cable became popular in the mid-'80s. Our smaller TVs were analog with black and white screens. None of our TVs had remote controls because they didn't exist then. We would have to get up and walk across the room to change the channel by turning the knob to the channel number we wanted. Everyone took turns getting up to change the channel. Most of the time, it was me who was picked to change the channel. We were so excited when the newer TVs came with remotes; that was a game changer.

The antenna for the main family TV was on the roof, and when it stormed, the picture would go bad. It would usually work itself out, but sometimes Dad would have to get on the roof to straighten it out. One of us would be under the back patio and the other at the end of the house yelling to each other when the picture was perfect so we could tell Dad to stop. The little TVs had their own antennas, "rabbit ears," so we could adjust to get a clearer picture.

On the music side in our house, we had a 1970s family stereo console with a dark brown decorative cabinet on the floor. It looked like a massive piece of furniture until the top opened to reveal a record player, radio, and 8-track player with storage space for albums. Lisa always laid on the floor and listened to her favorite records over and over. The crackling of the vinyl through the speakers was such a unique sound. Things changed when cassettes, cable TV, and VHS players came out in the '80s. These are the years that shaped our lives in so many ways.

As I had mentioned before, my family loved pictures. We had photo albums everywhere, from family vacations, birthdays, and just us kids having fun with our friends. Polaroids were neat because they were instant photos. We waited a few minutes for the image to become visible right before our eyes; we thought shaking them made it develop faster. *Maybe it did.*

Mom wrote when and where the photo was taken at the bottom of the picture. When compact cameras came out, Lisa had a Kodak that took 110 film. Sometimes I would sneak it out of our room and play with it. The cartridge had to be developed at the local drugstore, K&B. The older cameras had a flashbulb at the top which had to be replaced often. After we took the picture, we advanced the film to the next one by winding the little knob with our thumbs. It made it a little easier when disposable cameras came out since film was built in. Once all the photos were taken, we simply dropped the whole camera off to be developed.

We also had a great family camera that no one was allowed to touch. Dad usually loaded the 35mm film because it was tedious, and Mom didn't have the patience. They would buy a film cartridge based on how many photos and the needed exposure. After the roll was used, back to the drugstore to get it developed.

There were no do-overs if our eyes were closed. We had to wait till we got them back to see how we looked. We didn't know any different then, and there was always an element of surprise with at least a few photos. After picking up the pictures was when Lisa realized I had played with her camera.

God gave me the best parents and siblings and honestly the best friends a girl could ask for. They meant everything to me. We had a big family on my Dad's side with many aunts, uncles, and cousins. There were so many of us it was hard to keep everyone straight with who belonged with whom. Dad was one of nine kids, so family get-togethers and reunions were always big.

When I was born, my grandmother, Ruth had about twenty-five grandchildren, half of whom lived in Monroe. When I was younger, I hung out with my cousins a lot. We hung out at church, family birthday parties, and sometimes even a cousin sleepover. But as we all got older, we didn't spend as much time together since everyone was busy with their own lives. We always loved each other, and that never changed.

I have fond memories at my Aunt Carol's house. She built a shop in the backyard of her house where we did a lot of crafts. She and Mom loved making and painting ceramics. First, we would pick the mold we wanted to make, make up the ceramic mix, pour it in, and bake it in the kiln at high temperatures. Then we painted it and finished with a glaze. Lisa has several pieces Mom made that were handed down to her.

Aunt Carol's house and ours seemed to be where everyone got together. She always had a big Halloween party every year with a haunted house look in the front yard. When family from Texas and Florida visited, everyone came to our house. We had a big backyard with plenty of room to run around. Dad grilled out, and the adults would visit on the covered patio while we played. We even broke out the slip-n-slide on hot summer days.

Mom's side of the family was much different from Dad's because there were only three siblings; Mom was in the middle of her two brothers. She was the only sibling with kids, so, we were kind of spoiled. We spent a lot of time at my grandparents' house, about twenty minutes away, making it easy for all of us to get together. They lived in Lakeshore, off Highway 139, on Curve Drive. It was the same house my grandfather, Ziggy, built when they moved to Louisiana from Pennsylvania when Mom was thirteen. Lots of sweet memories were made there.

Every Sunday after church, we went over for lunch and the table would be set the same every week. My Grandmother, Rita, loved having her kids and grandkids together. She taught us how to set the table with plates and silverware. Ziggy was always cooking something in the kitchen with our grandmother. He made extra and took to people all over town who might not know where their next meal was coming from. Whenever our friends came with us, he constantly tried to feed them. He grew up during the Great Depression, and I'm pretty sure he went without a meal from time to time.

My uncles, George and Chris, both lived with my grandparents. George recently divorced and moved back after his marriage ended. Chris was younger, only two years older than Jerry. Chris and Jerry were almost like brothers, too, and went to the same school and were a grade apart.

Mom, Lisa, Grandmother Rita, and I made her famous nutbread every year around Thanksgiving. It was a whole weekend event at their house. It was my grandmother's family recipe that was handed down to her from her mother. She never shared it, and people would try to copy it but couldn't get it right. I helped roll out the dough and spread the nut mixture around so we could roll it up before it went into the oven. The whole house smelled of freshly baked bread. Once it was sliced, it looked like a pinwheel with nut filling. Most of the time, I made more of a mess than helped, but it was always fun. There would be loaves and loaves of nutbread that Mom and Dad shared with everyone. My grandmother made a big batch so everyone could take some. We would even keep some in the freezer to have later.

Every Christmas for as long as I can remember, we would spend Christmas Eve at their house and open our gifts after mass. I would still be wearing my angel costume with my halo and wings half crooked from the Christmas Eve Nativity service earlier that night. Christmas morning we spent at home after Santa came. Mom and Dad told us that we had to wait till 8 a.m. to get up to see what Santa had brought. We would call Time and Temperature at 318-325-9421 every two minutes to see if it was time to get up. We knew that number by heart. Christmas morning, Mom would make her famous monkey bread for breakfast, and we stayed in our PJs most of the day playing with our toys.

Some of my favorite toys were from the '80s. We got an Atari that we all shared and kept in the den. Frogger was my favorite, Lisa loved Donkey Kong, and Jerry was great at Asteroids. We spent hours and hours playing. The Rubik's Cube also came out in the '80s. Lisa got one in her stocking one year, and she tried and tried to solve it. One time she got so mad at me because I fooled her into thinking I had solved it, but actually I had taken off all the stickers and stuck them back on to look like I completed it. These were memories I would always treasure.

# CHAPTER 2

# The Early Days

Things seemed great at home, but unfortunately, my parents were having problems. My parents separated not long after we moved to the north side of town. It came out of nowhere when Mom and Dad sat all three kids down to tell us that Dad would move out for a while until they figured out everything. It was really confusing since we never saw them arguing. I was too young to understand what was happening, but things were different around the house for about a year and a half.

Dad rented an apartment in West Monroe, across the river. Lisa and I helped him get his apartment set up and decorated the room we shared. Jerry was already driving, so he could help Mom by getting Lisa and me around. We spent every other weekend at Dad's place. It wasn't the best situation, but they made it the best they could for us as they worked through their issues. They assured us that we didn't do anything to cause the breakup and they loved each other but needed some space to figure things out.

That's when Mom and Dad got us a dog to help make things a little better. He was the sweetest little miniature black poodle we named Coco. Honestly, having him to take care of was a nice distraction from what was going on at home. Our home just felt empty and broken.

Lisa was starting the fourth grade in Miss Roberts' class at Jack Hayes Elementary, next to the daycare. Lisa didn't know anyone at the new school, but she had met a friend who lived in the neighborhood over the summer, Angela. She lived one street over on Silver Drive. Mom reminded Lisa that she and Angela also went to Little Red School House in 1973 when they were four. Mom found a picture of them sitting together in their preschool class. The first person Lisa saw in class was Angela so she knew she would be OK. Lisa made several other friends in her class, like Melanie and Kim, and Melody, who was in another class. They would become some of her best friends when they got older.

Angela, however, helped Lisa during this time with our family. Her parents had also split up, and her Mom was getting remarried soon. They were inseparable, and I loved staying up with them when they had sleepovers. I wanted to be around Lisa and her friends all the time. It made me feel older, just like them. One of Angela's favorite meals at our house was my Mom's goulash which was hamburger meat and a mixture of leftover veggies from the fridge, but she loved it. A year later, her mom married and they moved to the neighborhood across the highway called Northside Terrace; they still hung out and were in the same circle of friends for years.

Life was so strange during this time. Mom and Dad both tried seeing other people off and on. It was so weird seeing them sitting next to someone else holding hands and laughing like my parents used to. I was still pretty young, so it didn't faze me as much. Lisa struggled a lot. I remember she had a lot of stomachaches. It was about once a month when she was back at the doctor with Mom and Dad complaining, and the doctor couldn't find anything physically wrong. After talking with the doctor, he concluded that she was subconsciously trying to get Mom and Dad back together. They both showed up at the appointments together, which was Lisa's way of hopefully making them fall back in love.

Our family doctor referred them to a psychologist so Lisa could get tested. She was embarrassed having to leave school early for two solid weeks. She made up stories about why she had to go every time. Honestly, between the three of us, I think she struggled the most, or at least it seemed that way. Jerry wasn't around much. He was a teenager working for a local mechanic after school, so he got home later.

We all had our chores which we were expected to do. My chore was keeping our room picked up, Jerry's was laundry, and Lisa's was helping with dinner. One time dad came over to pick us up, and a guy Mom was seeing was there, and everything blew up. I thought they were going to fight right there in our living room. It was just an awful situation. Dad tried dating a few women, but no one held a candle to Mom.

After a year and a half apart, with the help of a family counselor, Mom and Dad decided to give their marriage another try. Dad packed up everything, moved out of his apartment, and returned home where he belonged. We transitioned back into family life like before, and I could tell things were better with them. It's funny, not knowing before they were having problems, it was apparent that they were much better. Our home just felt right again.

I started Kindergarten at the Little Red School House, which was great because I would still get to go to work with Mom and be with her all day. I was spoiled, and liked how I was the manager's kid. Sometimes I would think I was in charge, too, until I was reminded that I was only in kindergarten. I always told my teachers I could skip nap time because my Mom was the boss. Mom would remind me later that when we were at work, I would be treated just like the other kids. No favoritism, no fun.

Lisa was now in the sixth grade at Jack Hayes Elementary, right next door. She walked over after school and hung out till Mom got off work. She helped with the babies to pass the time before we went home. Sometimes Lisa would ride the bus home and stay at the house until we got home so she could get started on her homework. Most of the time, she changed her clothes and went outside for a few hours with her friends. She was becoming a teenager, but I wasn't old enough yet to go home with her.

Lisa and I had both never met a stranger. Growing up in that environment taught us how to get along with others and develop relationships. I made friends easily and loved being around people.

One fond memory I have of the daycare was snack time. Tang orange drink and saltine crackers were our afternoon snacks after naps. Sometimes we got animal crackers as an extra treat. I always helped Miss Mary in the kitchen. She was the sweetest black woman who always smiled and was the first person I saw every morning. She made scrambled eggs and cinnamon toast for the kids who got dropped off before breakfast. She made the best meatloaf, putting cheese slices in the middle so it tasted like a cheeseburger. Mom tried doing it at home but never mastered how Miss Mary did it. Her kindness was infectious, and you couldn't help but smile anytime you were around her. I'm not sure if I ever told her how she impacted my life.

# CHAPTER 3

# The '80s

Growing up in the early to mid-'80s was fun with two older siblings. My sister's friends had a crush on our big brother, Jerry, especially when he was outside working on his car. He was a mechanic, so he was always out doing something to his car with his shirt off and cut-off denim shorts. His car was a 1981 Trans Am, like the one from *Smokey and the Bandit* but candy apple red with a black eagle on the hood and a sunroof. He washed it weekly to keep it nice and shiny. The boom box next to him blared Queen's "Another One Bites the Dust," and my friends and I would sing like rockstars at the top of our lungs. It was cool having a brother who was fourteen years older than me. Sometimes he would let us help him wash it, but we ended up having a water fight. On the really hot days, we would drink out of the water hose.

When I started first grade, I went to Jack Hayes just like Lisa did. It was so fun riding the bus. I felt so grown up leaving the house with my big sister. We hung out at the bus stop on the next block over on Silver Drive. Lisa and I walked together and hung out until her friends showed up. I sat in the same spot every day, third row on the right, and Lisa sat in the back where the older kids went. Once we were dropped off at school, we went in different directions. She was on the other side of the school in junior high. We never saw each other during the day, but we had teachers who were sisters. She had Mrs. Robinson, and I had her sister Miss Ford.

I had so much energy as a child, hyperactive, I guess. Sitting still was hard for me, so when I started elementary school, my doctor suggested they put me on medicine to help me focus. My parents weren't happy about it, but we had to do it.

Sometimes I made mornings difficult, not wanting to swallow the pill. Mom found a plastic cup with a little ledge at the top for a pill to sit, and the pill went down naturally when you took a drink. That changed everything. The medicine helped me most of the time but I was wound up again by the end of the day. My friends could also tell when the medication wore off.

My Mom dressed me in tights and a cute dress often, and by the end of the day, the tights had holes in them, and the dress was filthy. My face always seemed to be dirty too. One time Miss Ford told her sister about me taking my tights off and putting them on my head, telling everyone I was the Easter Bunny. Needless to say,

Lisa was mortified when Mrs. Robinson told that story to her seventh-grade class.

That year I started wearing glasses. I also noticed I couldn't see the chalkboard when Miss Ford would give us homework. When I read my favorite books, the words were blurry and looked jumbled together. The eye doctor discovered there were a few things going on. I had developed a lazy eye, so he put a patch over my left eye to make my right eye stronger. Of course, I would run around the classroom pretending to be a pirate! I definitely kept Miss Ford on her toes. She probably was not sad when I finished the first grade.

I met one of my best friends at the beginning of second grade. The day I met Melanie was one I would never forget. She was new to our neighborhood, living one street over on Silver Drive, a few houses down from where Lisa's friend Angela had lived, and where we caught the bus. The first day she showed up and got on the bus, I could tell she was scared, so I asked her to sit with me on the third-row seat on the right, and we were inseparable after that.

Melanie's friendship came into my life at a good time. I don't think she ever knew how much her friendship meant to me. We were inseparable! She also sometimes went to Little Red School House with me, so we would walk over together after school until Mom got off. She would come home with me most Fridays and have a weekend sleepover with some of our other neighbor-hood friends. We would take turns which house we would have the sleepover, but whichever one it was, we always had fun. My sleeping bag with Strawberry Shortcake was my favorite. I got it for my birthday that year, along with a Strawberry Shortcake doll to match that smelled like strawberries when you squeezed her. Mom ordered us Johnny's Pizza, a local favorite, and picked it up for us on the way home from work.

After staying up late we would sleep in, but when we finally got up on Saturday mornings, Mom would let us make breakfast. We weren't allowed to touch the stove, but loved the Pillsbury cinnamon rolls in a can. Mom let us unroll them and place them on the cookie sheet. Sometimes while they were baking, I loved to take the little plastic cup, put my finger right in the middle, and eat the icing, which didn't leave much for the tops of the cinnamon rolls. Lisa would get so mad at me because she loved lots of frosting. We stayed in our PJs most of the morning watching our favorite Saturday morning cartoons. It was kind of a family thing we did on Saturdays, even if we had friends over; that never changed.

We all had our favorite cartoons to watch. As a family, we all loved *Scooby-Doo*, but personally, I loved the *Smurfs*. Everyone had a chance to watch their favorite. Dad kept the *TV Guide* in the pocket of his brown leather recliner so we could always see what shows were coming on and when. He would circle some of our favorite shows. It was hard to see the times, so I would use his magnifying glass, which he used for maps when we traveled, though I had to remember to put it back in the glovebox of the car.

When I was in the third grade, someone in my class gave me a sticker book with unicorns and rainbows for my birthday; that's when my unicorn obsession started. It didn't matter what it was–stickers, buttons, wind chimes, ceramic figurines–I had it. Not sure why, but I was always drawn to them my whole life. I even made a ceramic one for myself at my Aunt Carol's. I guess because they were so colorful and magical, mysterious, and beautiful. I had them everywhere and all my friends would bring me anything unicorn if they went on vacation, which helped me build up quite a collection. I loved that unicorns were unusual, rare, and unique, just like me.

My friends loved being around my big sister, Lisa, with her big, teased hair, style of clothes, and everything about her. She didn't know it, but I looked up to her. I wanted to be like her when I grew up. We had shared a room most of our childhood. We got along, but I would annoy her because I was always getting into her stuff when she was gone.

I loved that our Dad worked for Hostess. His truck would sit at the end of our driveway with a picture of a giant Twinkie and Ding Dong on the side. Lisa was embarrassed by the truck; Jerry didn't care, but my friends thought having a buffet of snacks in the driveway was so cool. Dad only had one rule for us, we had to wait till they expired since he couldn't put those on the shelves, but we didn't mind; they tasted the same to us. He would keep the expired stuff in a different place so we knew we could have anything from that shelf. My favorite was Twinkies. I honestly could eat them every day and usually did. I would have them with my go-to drink of choice, chocolate milk. Mom always kept a gallon of milk with Hershey's chocolate syrup in the refrigerator door.

Across the highway from Treasure Island was Moon Lake. It's where the teenagers hung out at night, and during the day, it was filled with ski boats and people fishing. My parents bought a beautiful white ski boat with yellow stripes in the summer of 1982. Most weekends in the summer, we took it across the highway to Moon Lake boat dock so we could water ski and float until the sun went down.

Mom filled our blue Igloo cooler with bologna sandwiches on Holsum white bread with mayo and cheese, a variety of our favorite potato chips, Capri Sun for me, TAB for Mom, and Lisa, Dad, and Jerry drank Coke. Mom also got the wax candy, little bottles filled with juice, for Lisa. She liked to keep them in the cooler, chew on the wax after the juice, put it across her teeth, and pretend she had braces.

I was too young to ski, but Mom and Dad would let me ride with Lisa on the tube as they pulled us behind the boat. Jerry was the only one brave enough to water ski. He would get brave and even slalom which was using only one ski.

Louisiana's bayous were dark and murky, so we had to be on the lookout for alligators and water moccasins hanging out on the banks of the sandbar. One time when I was about six, we were out on the water fishing, and Dad pulled up a catfish with a huge snake attached to it. Needless to say, we all started screaming. Dad remained calm as he steered the boat to the shore only to find a bed of snakes; it was so scary since Lisa was terrified of snakes. After that happened, we went back to the marina to head home. It was a while before Lisa went back out on the boat.

Mom and Dad made us three feel so special when it came to our birthdays. Mom let us pick our theme for the cake and would go to the cake decorating section at Walmart to see if they had the pans we wanted. We had different ones through the years. My favorite was my Rainbow Bright cake, Lisa had a Winnie-the-Pooh, and Jerry had a sports car on several birthdays. To make it look perfect, she had all food coloring to mix with the white icing, every shape and size with the tips and the decorating bags. She had an extensive collection of pans from our birthdays that she would also use to make cakes for my cousins and sometimes our friends if she had the time. It was a fun hobby for her.

I loved having sleepovers for my birthday party. When I was younger, I would crash Lisa's. She loved having a sleepover or, as we called them, a "pallet party". I wanted to be in the middle of them, staying up all night with the teenagers. I knew I probably annoyed her, but her friends always enjoyed me hanging out, not knowing what would come out of my mouth. When I was old enough to start having them, almost every year, that's what I did for my birthday. It became a tradition that I would continue through my early teen years.

One time I embarrassed Lisa so badly when we were at JCPenney that she literally wanted nothing to do with me. I had a very vivid imagination, and I sat in the laps of mannequins and conversed with them. Jerry laughed at me, but Lisa wanted to crawl under the table and act like she didn't know me.

Mom left Little Red School House after fifteen years and went to work at McKee Electronics in West Monroe in an office job and worked a second job at Service Merchandise, a retail store in Monroe that sold everything from jewelry, toys, and home furnishings. Mom worked in the jewelry department, which was cool because we got a big discount. Dad's schedule was different every day because of his route, so some nights, he would be late coming home too. The three of us kids held everything together.

As a family, when we were all at home, we had dinner together and shared how our day went. Some nights Lisa was in charge of dinner. Mom taught her how to make the basics, but she got a little too confident and almost caught the whole kitchen on fire trying to fry hamburgers. That was the end of her cooking with grease in a frying pan. She went back to her all-time favorite, chicken spaghetti. It was so yummy with Velveeta cheese and Ro-Tel tomatoes with the noodles.

At least one of us always had a friend over. Our house was the place everyone wanted to hang out. Now that I was old enough, I rode the bus home from school. Lisa drove now, too, and started high school at Ouachita. Our parents bought her a red 1977 Honda CVCC when she was sixteen; it was a great first car and got her where she needed to go. The stick shift initially made it a little harder to drive until she got the hang of it. Dad and Jerry installed a cassette player in it since it just had a radio. Lisa and her friends piled in and ran all over town. She said she had ten people in that car, including her; not sure how they did that.

Mom and Dad made a deal with us kids that they would buy our first car, but after that, we would have to pay for our own. Lisa would take me to piano lessons when Mom worked late. I cherished our time together, driving around listening to our favorite songs and not having a care in the world. Lisa took piano lessons when she was eight for several years but lost interest in it. Because of my love of music, I wanted to take lessons, and really enjoyed them except for the practicing part. That was my downfall; I could never sit still and focus, a common theme in my life.

Most afternoons when we got home from school, I headed outside before dark to meet my friends and circle the island just like Lisa used to do. My baby blue 10-speed bike was a hand-me-down from Lisa. As the sun started to go down, the fireflies lit up the sky before the mosquitos took over. That was our signal to go inside.

I loved Lisa's friends as much as mine, and they loved me. Lisa, Melanie, who we called Mel to avoid confusion, and Melody loved going Friday nights to Skatetown on 165, not far from where we lived to see all their friends from Jack Hayes. Sometimes they squeezed Melanie and me into the back seat of Lisa's little car and took us with them. We loved walking in with them. They always made us feel special until the cute boys walked up, and then they acted like we didn't exist, but we knew it was just part of being a teenage girl.

Mom and Dad's marriage was better than ever. We did more things together again. They joined a weekly bowling league, and that's how the Bayou Bowl became our favorite hangout and a big part of my life. It was great since it was right across the highway from our neighborhood. The smell of burnt popcorn and pizza was the first thing you noticed when you walked in, and you could hear all of the video games dinging and buzzing. My friends from school were always there. Honestly, Bayou Bowl is where I met some of my best friends.

When Melanie and I were old enough, we joined the Junior league. I was actually pretty good. Lisa and Jerry didn't inherit the bowling gene. They could barely get a score over a hundred. Finally, something that I could do better than them. Dad taught me how to keep score with the little pencils with no eraser and the tiny paper with lines for names and scores. There was no room for mistakes.

An X was for a strike which didn't happen too often for me. When it did happen, my friends would laugh at me every time I got a strike; I would turn around and jump three times. That became my signature move.

The bowling alley was where I met my friend Sabrina. She moved to Louisiana from Maryland in the fifth grade and went to Jack Hayes, but we were in different classes. We saw each other on the playground and started hanging out. We became great friends, and she joined the bowling league with Melanie and me. Our team was called "Spare Us," which was Melanie's idea. We even made it to the state tournament in Lafayette and won!

Bowling was such a big part of my life. I literally spent my teenage years at the Bayou Bowl, and they hired me to help in the nursery when I was old enough; I loved hanging with the kids. I still wasn't old enough to be completely alone in the nursery, but I was there to help the older teenagers.

My dream was to get married one day and have a houseful of children. But until then, I chased boys. I had a crush on a cute guy named John from my class. He had black hair and was a little taller than me. Being in the sixth grade, I was way too young to be serious, so we just hung out, which was fine with me. We met on the weekends to play video games before I had to work. My favorite was Pac Man, and John loved Super Mario Brothers. Major perks of working at the bowling alley were unlimited video game tokens, free shoe rental, and half-priced food. John and I stayed friends even after the crush wore off. I had some of the best guy friends a girl could ever have, but never really had a serious boyfriend.

Music was my other love! I was always surrounded by it. My siblings and I had a massive cassette collection with all genres of music. Some of the cassettes were mixtapes with all of our favorite songs on them.

Jerry had a double cassette boombox, so we could record from one to the other. Lisa had me call the radio station and request Wham!'s "Wake Me Up Before You Go Go," or "Girls Just Wanna Have Fun" by Cyndi Lauper, or whatever was popular that week. We would wait and wait; sometimes, it would be an hour before it would play, so we had to be ready with a blank cassette in the boom box to hit RECORD at just the right moment. It was hard not to catch the commercials or the DJ talking, but we did the best we could. Lisa and her friends had the best mix tapes, which they'd share with each other.

Sidenote: nothing was worse than trying to wind a cassette back up using a No. 2 pencil after the tape got caught up in the player and unraveled.

I honestly didn't have a favorite genre; I loved all of them. One day I would listen to Van Halen and the next pop, and sometimes even a little Dolly Parton and Kenny Rogers, but overall, my favorite artist was Prince. *Purple Rain* came out in 1984 when I was eight. I was way too young to watch the movie, but my sister had the soundtrack on vinyl and cassette, so she played it over and over. When I got a little older, I loved Prince as much as she did. I blared "Purple Rain" as loud as I could from my stereo, which probably had some influence on my favorite color, purple.

Growing up in the '80s and early '90s, it was cool to see the transition from cassette to CD. Lisa and Jerry had gone from 8-track to vinyl to cassette. Between us, we had a vast collection of each lying around the house.

*Footloose* was one of my favorite movies that came out in 1984. It was full of music and dancing, two of my favorite things. Mel brought over her brothers, Michael and Mark, who were close to my age, and we watched *Footloose* over and over on the VCR.

Have I mentioned how much I loved fashion? If it was able to be bedazzled, we did. Lisa had a Bedazzler kit with lots of colored rhinestones, and she let us play around with it. We came up with our own original designs. Melanie and I were known to always be a little different from everyone else, and we thought that was cool.

Here's a good example. We bought a pink pair and yellow pair of Converse high tops and switched them out, so we each wore two different colors. There were a lot of raised eyebrows at first, but then everyone at school started copying us. Guess we were trendsetters. *Who knew?*

We designed for other people too. Melanie's brother and his friends paid us to tie-dye their shirts and bleach their jeans. It was always fun seeing what we could come up with.

Some days I'd sneak into my sister's closet and wear her clothes; she never knew we played dress-up when she left for work. Lisa was barely off the island before we dug through her stuff. We spent all day in her room playing with her clothes and made sure her things were strategically placed exactly where we found them.

Honestly, though, when she couldn't find her things, they were usually on my side of the closet. She had acid-washed jeans that were high-waisted and pegged at the bottom and Nike high tops. Jeans of all colors were trendy. Lisa's closet looked like a box of crayons. Leggings and long shirts were also the look. Lisa wasn't a complete fashionista, but she made whatever look she had her own, and I was the same.

As I got older, my fashion style changed, and I started wearing rock-n-roll t-shirts, Justin cowboy boots, and jeans all the time. It became my signature look. Lisa loved rock-n-roll, too, and collected many cool t-shirts from concerts she had gone to. If I asked her nicely, she'd give me permission to borrow them. Cinderella played at the Monroe Civic Center and Lisa, Melody, Mel, her brothers and I went to our first concert. That was a night I would never forget. We lost our hearing temporarily for a day since no one told us we should wear earplugs; we knew for next time.

Fall of 1985, as the leaves turned colors and the temperatures cooled, my brother got his own apartment with his friend, Tony. Jerry and his girlfriend Rhonda, who dated a few years before, were back together and would soon be married. I missed my brother, but I gained my own room. For the first time ever, I would have my own space to do whatever I wanted, within reason of course.

Mom and Dad sold the matching furniture Lisa and I had to their friends who had small kids and used that money to buy new furniture for our new spaces. Lisa wanted a waterbed like our parents had, so they bought her a King size with built-in shelves as the headboard. Her walls were full of posters of her favorite bands, Van Halen, Mötley Crüe, Poison, and that famous poster of David Lee Roth from Van Halen in a pool where it looked like he wasn't wearing any clothes.

I got a queen-sized bed, Prince posters on the wall, and my unicorns were everywhere. I even found unicorn sheets at Walmart. My built-in desk was a great place to display my collection and do my homework. There was even enough room for me to have my own stereo, a turntable, CD with cassette player so I was able to play a little bit of everything. I had my own TV. It wasn't a color picture, but that didn't matter. It was all mine. I usually kept it on MTV to watch all my favorite videos.

In 1987, when *Dirty Dancing* came out, Melanie and I had just turned eleven, and we were too young to go to the movies, so we had to wait till it was released on HBO. Lisa recorded it on our VCR player so she and her friends could watch it, but sometimes we would stay up late to watch it, even though we weren't supposed to. We were obsessed with everything about it! I wanted to be Penny, and she wanted to be Baby. It became my favorite movie of all time! We watched it over and over. We never got tired of it! We practiced all the dances and knew every word of every song. That summer, Melanie went on vacation with us, and we pretended the campground we went to was Kellerman's.

That same year, Lisa graduated high school in May, and Jerry and his wife welcomed a baby girl, Meghan, in June. Our family was growing, and I couldn't be more excited about becoming an aunt. My friend Sabrina went on our family vacation to Six Flags in Texas. We had so much fun riding all the big rides. I loved roller coasters, so between she and Dad they would ride with me.

Sometimes we walked to the island's entrance across the highway to the railroad tracks hoping our parents wouldn't find out since it wasn't safe. Ninety-five percent of the time, my friends and I did everything we were supposed to, but that five percent, we made them count by doing something stupid.

For instance, when Melanie and I were almost fourteen, we met some really cute older guys at the bowling alley; they were seventeen, and we told them we were sixteen. One night, they wanted to pick us up from the bowling alley and take us for a ride around town. Our plan seemed flawless to us; I told my parents I was staying with her, and she told her parents she was staying with me. We walked to the bowling alley across the highway. They picked us up and took us, God-knows-where. We were so trusting and gullible!

We thought we had pulled it off when we returned to the bowling alley around 11 p.m. We didn't know that our moms found out what we were up to, and since Melanie's dad was working nights, *my* Dad got in his Toyota truck and drove all over town looking for us. He spotted us in the back seat of the guy's car, did a U-turn on Hwy 165 and chased us down. I had never seen my Dad that mad; it wasn't his nature. He yanked the driver out, slammed him against the car, and told him and the other two guys, in very descriptive words, to never come near us again! We were both grounded forever! Needless to say, we learned our lesson.

## CHAPTER 4

# A Change of Scenery

Fall of 1990 I started junior high. *How was it possible that I was a seventh grade?* There were such fond memories at Jack Hayes Elementary School. I made some of my best childhood memories and had the best friends a girl could ask for.

The school system had changed since Lisa was in junior high. It was now separated with grades one-six at Jack Hayes, seven-eight at Ouachita Junior High and nine-twelve at Ouachita High School. I was moving to Ouachita Junior High in the same building where my parents and Lisa had gone to high school. Lisa was the last class to attend high school there before it was turned into the junior high.

I may not have been the best student grade-wise, but I could tell you my teachers never forgot me. I was

nervous about starting at a new school with more people. Some had come from Jack Hayes, but others came
from other elementary schools. Melanie and Sabrina
were both going, so I knew it would be OK having two
of my best friends with me.

One of Lisa's teachers from Jack Hayes, Mrs. Daniel,
had transferred to the junior high to teach PE (physical
education) in 1987, so it was nice to see a familiar face.
She asked me if I was Lisa's little sister. Boullt wasn't a
very common name. She realized right off how different
Lisa and I were; I was more of the daredevil. Mrs. Daniel
called me *"Lightning Bolt"* just like Lisa, and we formed a
tight bond just like they had. I would never forget her as
a teacher. She definitely made an impact on me.

As the year went by, Melanie, Sabrina, and I did a lot
together, but we started meeting other people; Melanie
and I drifted apart. We hung out in the neighborhood,
but we had different groups of friends at school. I still
loved Prince, but my posters changed to Guns N' Roses.
I loved Axl Rose, and "Welcome to the Jungle" was my
jam! Seventh grade flew by so fast. I really loved junior
high and was looking forward to the eighth grade.

I actually started to feel more like a grown-up. Lisa
would let me hang out with her friends more as I got
older. The movie *Ghost* came out and since I loved Pat-
rick Swayze from *Dirty Dancing*, Lisa and Mel invited
me to go with them. It was PG-13 and I had just turned

thirteen, so I genuinely felt like one of the older girls. We called the Cinema III theater for the recorded movie showing times to see what time worked best for us.

I was grateful for these special times because things at home became different again. Lisa was gone more often with her friends and had a new boyfriend, Mike, so we didn't see her as much. She spent a lot of time at our grandparent's house since his grandparents were best friends with ours and lived next door to each other. I missed having my siblings around and the way things used to be, but they were on their own paths.

Mom and Dad worked long days and were rarely home at the same time. Usually, I was with one of them every night but some nights it would be just me and Coco till they got home. I became pretty independent and was OK being by myself for a few hours.

1991 started off really fun for Lisa. Her friend from high school, Catherine, won a contest on the local radio station for an all-expense paid trip to Los Angeles for the American Music Awards and invited Lisa to go with her. They would be sitting in the same room with all our favorite musicians. A trip of a lifetime! Neither of them had flown before, so this experience would be one they never forgot. Lisa called home from the hotel's bathroom phone to let us know they had arrived safely. She thought it was hilarious that a phone was next to the toilet.

That weekend started with attending soundcheck and watching INXS rehearse, then it was back to the hotel room to get ready for the show. Arriving at the Shrine Auditorium in Los Angeles about an hour before the show so they could find their seats, an usher showed them where they were sitting, and they ran right into Gene Simmons and Paul Stanley from KISS. As they proceeded to their seats, they stood next to New Kids on the Block, Flavor Flav, Gloria Estefan, and Wilson Phillips, to name a few.

However, the best part of the night was after the show was over Catherine decided to grab hold of a group of artists walking backstage and then she disappeared. Lisa stood in the auditorium lobby not sure what to do. The ushers tried to make her leave, but she explained she was waiting for her friend. About fifteen minutes later, Catherine returned to the lobby with a plan. She got stamped as she left the after party, found Lisa and did the lick, stick, and roll on the back of her hand to transfer the stamp. They would only know if it worked when they got to the party. It worked! They made it through two security lines and ended up at the backstage party after the awards.

They were literally right next to some of the biggest musicians in the 1990s. Lisa met her favorite twins, Nelson, and said she was a little speechless. Dick Clark stopped and chatted with them; even one of the rock bands asked them to ride in their limo. I think one of them wanted to go, and the other didn't think it was a good idea; they never told me which one didn't want to go.

The next day they walked around Los Angeles and saw some of the famous landmarks like Grauman's Chinese Theatre with stars and actors' handprints and autographs in cement down the sidewalk. They came home with lots of fun stories and had all of us laughing for hours.

When we rewatched the awards we recorded on VHS, we could see them sitting in the audience with their big, blonde hair next to all the entertainers. I couldn't wait until they got their pictures developed to see all the fun they had. I think this trip made Lisa realize she wanted to be in the entertainment business.

This same year Dad taught me how to drive. I tried driving occasionally, but we never had one-on-one drive time together. He drove us out of the neighborhood since there wasn't a red light to get across over the interstate. Lisa let me try to drive her Sunbird that she bought after the bad wreck she had in 1988. It was easier to navigate than Dad's big Chevy truck, but he wanted me to be comfortable in every car I drove, so we drove his truck, too. He got out and switched places at Moon Lake, where we used to put the boat in. I struggled to keep the truck in the middle of the lane and hugged the middle line too much, so he taught me a trick. His truck had a seam in the middle of the hood, and he told me to take that seam and line it up to the yellow line in the middle. I did it and was directly in the center of the lane. It was a trick I would always use.

In August 1991, I got my driver's permit at fifteen and could drive with a parent or my siblings in the car, so I got plenty of practice. I knew then I wanted to drive something bigger and higher off the ground. I didn't want to take after my siblings when it came to driving and vehicles, though. Jerry had gotten so many speeding tickets, and his Trans Am had been stolen from Forsythe Park when he decided to leave it with the keys in it to ride around with friends. It was found three months later in the Ouachita River. Lisa burned a pecan orchard a few years earlier and totaled her Toyota Corolla. My goal was to be a better driver than they were.

That was the fall that I met Jennifer. She had gone to Jack Hayes, but we were never in the same circle of friends. I had seen her a few times at the bowling alley, but we didn't know each other until we had the same class in eighth grade. Sabrina, Melanie, and Jennifer were not close friends separately, so I was the common bond. Jennifer and I became inseparable and the best of friends. Sabrina had a serious boyfriend I didn't care for, so we didn't hang out as much anymore. I also met Melissa around this time, who was a year older and lived in the same apartment complex as Jennifer. We three became inseparable and were often called The Three Musketeers, or sometimes we would pretend to be EnVogue, singing and dancing. Seems like I was always singing and dancing; that was a common thing with me.

October of that year, my big sister left our home on Jolly Roger and moved to Tennessee with her boyfriend to start their life together. I was devastated but happy for her at the same time. Though we fought like cats and dogs most of the time, I missed her terribly. She was indeed my best friend.

Before she moved, Lisa and Catherine surprised me with tickets to see Poison. I was shocked. They were one of the hottest hair bands, and were coming to the Monroe Civic Center. We had great seats, but it didn't matter because we never sat down. We sang every song at the top of our lungs and just about lost our voices. It was the best concert I attended, and only the second one. Somehow, we made it backstage to meet some of the band. Wow, what an incredible experience! They had become experts at being backstage. It was our last time hanging out, and I was so glad they took me along.

Lisa and Mike packed up their stuff that would fit in a small trailer and moved 550 miles away from us that fall. They moved to a cute little town about an hour east of Nashville called Gordonsville, where they lived with his Dad, who had moved a few years earlier. It was a way for them to start their life together without rushing to find their own place.

My heart was broken; my big sister, whom I admired, was no longer at home. *Did I tell her how much I loved her before she left? Did she know that I thought she could do no wrong? She knew, right?* We talked quite a bit during the first few months because though she didn't want to admit it, she was homesick. She had never been that far away from home for that long. She ended up getting a part-time job at a local health club, Sports Village, where she made some new friends and was able to find something she knew how to do. During high school, she worked at Atlantis Health Club in Monroe, so she had experience, and talking to people came easy to Lisa too. We definitely had that in common.

We were first in line the day I turned sixteen to take the driving test. I passed with flying colors and got my driver's license. It was official, and I couldn't have been more excited. When we got home that afternoon, my parents surprised me with a 1989 red Chevy S10 Blazer, my dream vehicle! One of Jerry's friends was selling it, so Jerry checked it out before Mom and Dad bought it. He cleaned it and drove over to the house while I took my test so it would be sitting in the driveway when we got back. I couldn't believe it; I started crying when I saw it sitting there. My dream vehicle was sitting in our driveway with a big, red shiny bow on top.

They handed me the keys, with a unicorn key chain, of course. It even had a combo cassette/CD player. I started collecting CDs after I got my combo stereo and portable CD player called a Sony Discman, which replaced my Sony Walkman that only played cassettes. When I got in, Jerry passed some of his favorite cassettes/CDs down to start my own collection to keep in my Blazer. Lisa left a box of CDs too, so I went through them and picked out my favorites.

I loved driving with the windows down, listening to music, singing, and driving on the back country roads. Most of my friends didn't have their licenses yet, so I was usually the chauffeur. A month later, I started high school; Ouachita High School was so much bigger than the junior high. It would be the first time I drove myself to school though I wasn't allowed to drive any friends to school at first, but eventually, my parents let me. My parents didn't want any distractions while I was just starting to drive; I stayed distracted enough without any help.

During this time, things at home were changing too. My niece, Meghan, who was my little sidekick, was now four, and I took her everywhere! They lived on the outskirts of town on the Bayou; Jerry was a local trucking company manager, and Rhonda worked at State Farm. I often babysat for gas money.

Lisa was settled in Tennessee. She and Mike realized they were too young for such a serious relationship, so they decided to call it quits, staying friends since our families were so close. She loved Tennessee and knew this would be her home, and also knew she wanted to go back to school and finish her degree that she started at NLU. She rented a cute little one-bedroom apartment in Lebanon, Tennessee working full time at Sports Village since her commute was only five minutes instead of thirty. Her co-workers become her second family. Everyone made her feel at home.

Now that she would be living in her own place, she asked if we could bring her some of her stuff. Her room at home was still the same except for her clothes and some personal items. Dad drained her king-sized waterbed, took it piece by piece, and placed it in the back of his truck, careful not to tear a hole in the mattress. He loaded up the dresser and mirror, too.

Mom and I took turns driving Dad's truck to Tennessee. We had so much fun on that trip. We shopped to get Lisa set up with everything she didn't have, hitting local garage sales and thrift stores to piece together the necessities. Mom found her a wooden table with matching chairs for her kitchen and a small loveseat couch that had a twin foldout bed for when we came to visit.

We stayed for several days unpacking boxes, putting her waterbed back together, and decorating her tiny one-bedroom apartment on Toshiba Drive. That's all she needed, and it was perfect.

It was weird not having my family together. There were no more family dinner nights, weekends on the boat, family vacations, or bowling leagues. Without my siblings there and me being gone a lot, my parents realized their marriage was over. They drifted apart again, and now, ten years after their first separation, they decided they both needed a new start. They filed for divorce, and this time Mom moved out. Their divorce was final in December of 1992, and once again, my world changed as I knew it.

# CHAPTER 5

# *Family Dynamics*

Our lives were so different; the family we once knew wasn't together. Divorce wasn't something that happened in my group of friends, but it happened to us. On paper, we weren't your typical American family anymore, but we were still family.

We sold the Jolly Roger home I had lived in since I was three in early 1993 after the divorce. I was so sad leaving the house but cherished the memories there. I walked around the backyard reminiscing the fun times we had. Our childhood playhouse that Dad built still stood and was ready for the next family's kids. The memories of lying on the roof with Crisco and baby oil slathered on to get a suntan, because that's what Lisa did. The missing palm tree that my cousin Jared and I accidently burned down when we were young, the above ground pool that Mom swam in with us and pulled Meghan around on a raft, the big yard we all had to mow when we were old enough, all the thumbtack holes in the walls from all of our posters, the carport where Dad and Jerry worked on all of the cars and so many more flooded through my brain.

Life as I knew it was forever changing. I decided to live with my Mom full-time and stay with my Dad every other weekend. Mom and I lived in a small two-bedroom house with one bathroom across the river in West Monroe; since it was just the two of us, it was OK. Mom and Dad divided the home décor so there were pieces at each place that reminded me of home. Mom kept the Autumn Fall picture, and Dad got the owl pictures.

Living in West Monroe, I was further from most of my friends, but since I could drive, we saw each other often. My Dad rented a cute little two-bedroom, blue house close to the college, Northeast Louisiana University. He lived alone, but I stayed with him every other weekend. It would be perfect when I went to college and could move in with Dad full time.

The only thing that felt right was Sabrina and her family moved to West Monroe a few months before we did, one street over from our house, and we would start our sophomore year together. I didn't love the idea of starting at West Monroe, but I didn't have much choice. Most weekends, Sabrina and I drove to Jerry's and babysat

Meghan. She always wanted to watch the *Little Mermaid* over and over. We knew every song from that movie.

Jennifer was pregnant and dropped out of school our freshman year with a baby coming soon, and I was going to start at West Monroe High School for my sophomore year. Melissa had a serious boyfriend and planned to marry in the fall; they lived close to Dad. She asked Jennifer and me to be bridesmaids for her November wedding.

Both of my friends were doing things I dreamed of doing one day, getting married and having a baby. It was so much fun to be a part of their experiences. Jennifer and I would play music for her baby, and her stomach would move to the beat. It was so cool! Her baby girl, Sage, was born in late June of 1993. I spent the second night in the hospital with them to help her. Jennifer needed to rest so I was there to help with Sage until it was feeding time. It was so sweet seeing Jennifer as a mom. I would help babysit Sage as much as I could.

That summer, I went to Nashville to see Lisa several times. Me, Dad, and Sabrina helped her move into a bigger apartment in the complex next door, a two-bedroom, so she had room for us and any other friends who came to visit. She showed us around and took us to the Opryland Hotel and the Grand Ole Opry.

In July, I needed a change of scenery, so I asked her if I could come to stay with her for a few weeks. Mom decided she wanted to move to Tennessee for a new start, so we drove eight hours, and left me there for three weeks. Lisa was all set up in her two-bedroom apartment, and I had my own room all to myself. I wanted to get to know Tennessee more since I would be living there soon.

While she was at work, I went into her closet just like old times. It made me laugh thinking about how Melanie and I would play dress up for hours when we were kids. Some days I dropped Lisa off at work and drove around, hoping not to get lost. I stayed in a ten-mile radius of her apartment, remembering specific landmarks in case I got turned around. Her apartment wasn't far from the Cracker Barrel home office; I was good to go when I found that. I met some of her Tennessee friends when they came over to play board games and Lisa made her chicken spaghetti like she did when we were kids.

Lisa and I had the best time! We laughed till we cried. I felt like we were more like friends than sisters. She saw me as a young woman instead of her annoying little sister. We even rented some of our favorite movies while growing up, like *Dirty Dancing* and *Purple Rain*. So many blessings!

Three weeks went by so fast, and I was sad to leave, but I knew I would see her in just a few short months when we moved there. Dad came to pick me up and stayed a few days with his girls. We went to the Opryland Hotel again, and someone took one of my favorite pictures of us that I ended up framing later. Dad and I had the best time on our ride back, stopping often to switch out so I could help drive. He spent his adult life driving all over for his job, so he liked it when I drove for a while.

This would be the last time for a while that we would have together. Dad was sad that I would be so far away, but he understood why Mom needed a change and knew being with Lisa would be good for all of us. Looking back on that summer, it was probably the best summer of my life! I was again reminded of all my blessings.

As summer ended, the days were getting shorter, and everyone got back into school mode. No more long weekends, summer vacations, or staying up way past our bedtime. I was getting ready to start my sophomore year of high school. Everything looked different: a new home, a new school, a friend with a baby, and a friend getting married. Jennifer and I went with Melissa helping her pick out her wedding dress. It was such a special experience. We found our bridesmaids' dresses, too; long, pink satin with puffy sleeves, and our shoes were the same color satin, just like the dresses.

I'd soon turn seventeen and was so excited about my future! I had big dreams and knew I was going to make a difference!

I started West Monroe High School in the fall of 1993. I loved Ouachita, and now going to the rival school across the river just didn't feel right. I only had one friend, Sabrina, which was great, but she was still dating a guy I didn't like, so our time together was few and far between those days. I begged Mom to let me go back to Ouachita, but the school zoning didn't allow it. We discussed me staying with Dad more during the week because his house was in my old school zone. She promised that we would discuss it as a possibility. Which wasn't a no, so there was some hope.

And then, on November 7, 1993, everything I knew changed forever!

# CHAPTER 6

## *Last Call*

A trip to Nashville, Tennessee, on Friday, November 5, 1993, took Mom and Jerry to look for places to live before the big move. Mom had taken a new position with her company, Service Merchandise, at the corporate office in Brentwood, Tennessee, south of downtown Nashville. Mom worked part-time at Service Merchandise for many years, so this was an excellent opportunity to go full-time on the corporate side. She knew she wanted an apartment close to her new job until deciding what part of town she eventually wanted to live in. They had one weekend to find that perfect place.

Lisa saved local newspapers with apartment listings and circled ones in the area Mom wanted. Mom brought Jerry with her to ensure they were looking in the right places; she was directionally challenged sometimes, and she wanted to make sure she would have an easy commute to the office. Jerry drove so Mom could look at the listings and make sure they went to the right place. Sidenote: this was before GPS or phones that told us where to go. This happened to be the same weekend as Melissa's wedding, so I was excited about spending one last weekend with the girls before I moved with Mom to Tennessee.

Deep down, I wasn't thrilled about moving to Tennessee; honestly, I dreaded it. I didn't want to leave my friends but I knew it was the best thing for all of us at the time. This was the new start Mom needed since the divorce, and Tennessee was the perfect place to do that. I was glad that we would be back together with Lisa. That was the only bright side to all of this.

Mom planned to move in mid-November before Thanksgiving and start her new job the first week of December. I packed my room to make it easier, knowing I would be busy with the wedding the whole weekend before. I rolled up all my clothes and wrapped all my breakable unicorns with the Sunday comics, and my photo albums put up, placing them in boxes and carefully stacking them against a wall in our house. I kept some of my favorite CDs out to listen to on the long drive to Tennessee. Another chapter of my life ended with an empty bedroom and everything I owned in ten boxes.

The wedding was the same weekend in November as Mom and Jerry's trip. We had fun things planned before Melissa's big day. The weather was a little crisp, so it would make for a beautiful wedding outdoors on the edge of the Bayou. It would be a colorful backdrop with the sunset peeking through the mossy trees on the water. Friday night, we planned a slumber party, where we'd paint our nails, watch romantic movies, and eat our favorite, Johnny's Pizza. Like any other Friday night, around 10:30 p.m., I called Lisa's apartment to check in with Mom to say I was home and let her know we were in for the night. We ended our conversation with the usual, "I Love You, talk to you tomorrow," and then hung up like we always did.

About an hour later, we were ready to call it a night when the phone rang. It was an ex-boyfriend of Jennifer's, Tre. He wanted us to go to the levee at Moon Lake with his friend Ret. Deep down, I felt it wasn't the best idea, but they reminded me Mom was out of town and I had already "checked in" for the night; she would never know. I agreed to go.

They picked us up in a 1988 4-door Ford Taurus; Melissa in front with Tre and Ret, Jennifer, and I were in the back seat, and somehow, I ended up in the middle. This was the first time we had met Ret. He went to River Oaks High School with Tre.

Around midnight, we ended up at the levee, where kids our age hung out. It was a place where we could be ourselves and where no one would bother us. This was a popular spot where all the local teenagers would go. We ran into a lot of people we knew.

After an hour, we left Moon Lake, and stopped at the Quick Stop to call another of Tre's friends, Justin. We swung by his house in Town and Country to pick him up and drove out to an abandoned bar in Swartz that was said to be haunted. It really didn't seem all that scary, so we hung out in the parking lot until the wee hours of the morning.

We got back in the car and drove around a few more hours, but around 5:30 a.m., when we dropped Justin off, Tre noticed his wallet was gone. He thought it must have fallen out at the abandoned bar, so we drove back toward Melissa's apartment, which wasn't too far from there.

It was almost 6 a.m., and I dozed off in the backseat with Ret to my left and Jennifer to my right. Melissa was in the front seat sound asleep too, and Tre was the only one awake. We were only about four miles from Melissa's apartment when life as we knew it changed in a split second.

At 5:55 a.m. Saturday, November 6, 1993, I felt something hit my head, then a loud crash, and everything went dark. At that moment, I had no idea what was going on. Melissa woke up on impact, screaming with glass from the shattered windshield in her mouth. We were in someone's front yard. Tre and Melissa got out and removed Jennifer from the backseat laying her on the ground, trying to calm her down. Melissa came to my side, held my head in her arms, and talked to me, hoping to wake me up.

I heard her but couldn't respond. I felt and heard the gurgling noises coming up from my mouth. I wished I could have responded to her. I felt myself slipping away slowly. Desperately wanting Melissa to hear my whisper and tell my family I love them in case I didn't make it, I wasn't even able to get those words out.

A few minutes passed and I heard sirens and people talking around me. *What happened?* Someone said, "He is not going to make it." Ret had been severely injured on impact from the car hitting the tree. Tre held his best friend praying for any response, but he wasn't responsive when the ambulance arrived. Tre told the police a dog ran out in front of him and made him swerve, but I think he had fallen asleep at the wheel and crossed over four lanes of traffic. No one really knew what had happened.

The night started out so fun but ended in tragedy as the sun came up on that chilly Saturday morning. At this point, I'm still not sure what happened. The emergency team placed me on a stretcher; my pulse was weak. I heard the police say, Tre swerved, missed the curve, hit a mailbox, impacted into a large pine tree on the left passenger side, and then spun 180 degrees for another forty-six feet and ended up facing south in someone's front yard on LA Hwy 139. Before the impact into the tree, the mailbox came through the back window and hit me in the head. That's when I blacked out.

I was literally lying there less than a mile from my grandparent's house. *Could they hear the sirens? Did they know it was me? Were they awakened by the loud crash? How would my family know where I was?* So many questions, and I wasn't even sure what was happening to me.

The team tried reviving me with CPR and shocking my heart. I wasn't responsive, though I had a faint pulse; they knew there was no time to waste. I watched them work on me, floating above everyone. They loaded me up into the ambulance and rushed me to St. Francis Hospital so I could get the care I needed. Melissa and Jennifer were taken to North Monroe Hospital, where they were treated and released, and Tre was being held for observation at St. Francis, a few floors down from where I was. Ret was pronounced dead on arrival at St. Francis.

# CHAPTER 7

# *ICU (I See You)*

*I* was in ICU at St. Francis Hospital in downtown Monroe and heard everything around me but wasn't awake. It felt like a bad dream . . . no, a nightmare. My parents couldn't be reached. Mom wasn't answering her home phone because she was in Tennessee. Dad worked early that morning on a route and wasn't home when they tried to call his house. An officer who knew Jerry called his house, but his wife, Rhonda, told him he was in Tennessee. The officer filled her in and Rhonda called Lisa's apartment with the news.

Lisa answered and gave the phone to Jerry. He stepped into the bathroom to have some privacy. Jerry couldn't believe what his wife told him. After he hung up, he called the hospital and spoke to the doctor, who explained the damage to my brain. He blacked out and fell into the bathtub. Lisa called to him. Waking up, he assured her he was OK and came out to fill Lisa in on what he was told. They both sat in disbelief. And Mom was nowhere to be found.

Lisa and Jerry tried to figure out where she had gone when she walked into the apartment with an armful of groceries. Lisa only had rice and green beans in her pantry, so she got up early and went to the grocery store.

When Jerry told her the news, she dropped everything, literally. The groceries hit the floor, as every muscle in her body went numb. It now made sense to her why she woke up at 5:55 a.m. with an uneasy feeling. Mom realized she woke up at the exact same moment the wreck happened, even though she didn't know that at the time. I never knew the connection between a mother and child until that moment.

My Dad had taken a supervisor position for the local coffee company, Community Coffee. Some of my favorite memories with Dad were helping him stock the shelves on his route; on Saturdays, he ran the route if no one was available, and this was one of those Saturdays. However, that morning his company couldn't find him. Finally, one of his co-workers knew which route Dad was on and called the grocery store in Delhi with a message that he needed to get to St. Francis immediately. He didn't know the severity of my condition, but he had a bad feeling in his gut.

Mom and Jerry got in the car almost immediately and were on their way back to Monroe. They hadn't even unloaded from the night before after their long drive to Nashville. It would be one of the longest eight hours of their lives. Lisa couldn't get it together quickly enough to ride with them, so Mom threw the cash she had saved for apartment deposits at her, and she was on the first flight from Tennessee to Louisiana. *What was happening? What was all this urgency about?* I wasn't awake, but I wasn't aware of what happened. I didn't understand the severity of my injuries.

The hospital waiting area was full of my aunts, cousins, and friends even before my immediate family arrived. Lisa called Mel, Melody, and Catherine that morning to tell them everything she knew and then called Delta Airlines to book the next flight to Monroe. Catherine would pick Lisa up at the airport just a few hours later. Melody ran into someone she went to church with that was working and got a few tidbits of information. Catherine asked as many questions as possible to prepare Lisa for what she was about to walk into. This was the first time some of my family met Lisa's friends they had heard about but never met.

Everyone prayed for me and spread the prayer chain all over town. My aunts used the phone in the lobby to call their friends on the prayer chain list to add my family and me to it. My cousins prayed for me in the hospital chapel.

Lisa was the first to arrive. Her flight landed in Monroe around 1 p.m., and she rushed to the hospital ICU with Catherine. Another one of her friends, Ellen, was a nurse on duty that day, so she filled her in and kept everyone informed. My Dad wasn't far behind Lisa and arrived about an hour later.

My Mom and brother were about halfway between Tennessee and Louisiana. They would stop and call from pay phones when they refueled. The waiting room was full of familiar faces praying for me and my family. I felt the love and prayers from everyone that came to the hospital. People I hadn't seen in a long time were there for support. Even though I couldn't talk, I heard everyone talking to me. I wanted so badly to tell them I could hear them. Lisa told me stories from when we were kids by my bedside.

One of her favorite stories to tell about me was the pantyhose on my head, the Easter Bunny story. Another favorite story Lisa told involved me sitting on department store mannequins' laps and talking to them. I probably embarrassed Lisa a lot, but it was all in fun. Truth be told, I was a little hyperactive and couldn't sit still, which showed up when I always got in trouble at school for talking too much. I just couldn't help it; I was always full of energy.

My friends came in one at a time to love on me and tell me crazy things we did when we were little. Oh, the stories they told. I had forgotten so many of them, but they came rushing back with laughter and love. They reminded me of all our fun sleepovers and how we stayed up all night watching our favorite movies.

Melanie and I hadn't hung out as much as we got older, but we were always friends; that never changed. I ran into her a few weeks earlier at the bowling alley, and we were able to catch up like time hadn't passed. She sat in my room and talked about *Dirty Dancing*, how we were Baby and Penny, and the time we pretended the campground was Kellerman's. Melanie laughed and cried as she told one of our stories.

Sabrina reminded me about the trips she had gone on when we were kids and the most recent one to Nashville, Tennessee. She told me I was one of the funniest friends she had ever met. Jennifer came by after the wedding, still banged up and bruised from the accident. She brought Sage to sit next to me and play the music we had played when Sage was in her belly. My cousins shared stories from our family reunions. My aunts came in one by one and held my hand and prayed over me.

Everyone who came to see me warmed my heart. I wish I could have told them how much it meant to me to see them there, how much I loved them, and how I cherished their friendships. Surely, they knew. I had told them, right?

Mom and Jerry arrived around 4 p.m. Saturday afternoon. I'm sure not knowing what they would find when they arrived made it the longest drive ever. Jerry pulled up to the hospital and Mom ran to the ICU as fast as she could. I was still on a ventilator and had very little brain activity.

My parents and siblings sat with the doctors to find out exactly what was happening. It didn't look good for me. *Is this how it was supposed to end?* Hours passed, and both my parents sat by my bedside praying with me, telling me funny stories as they held my hands. I felt their love radiate through my whole body. Even though Mom and Dad's marriage didn't work, they still loved each other. They shared intimate moments only between parent and child. I was a part of them, and they were a part of me.

Honestly, I looked like I was sleeping; it wasn't a traumatic scene from a movie. I didn't have one scratch or bruise from the wreck, just a large bump on my forehead from where the mailbox struck me, which was a blessing that I didn't look all banged up. It was probably harder to see me like that and realize there was so much damage on the inside.

Lisa sat in the room with Ellen when my face got really red, and she asked Lisa to step out. Lisa didn't have a good feeling after that happened. The doctors and nurses came in to see what was happening. My blood pressure had escalated, which wasn't a good sign.

The doctors left my room, and I heard them telling my family that because of the damage to my brain, it was unlikely I would survive. *Whoa, that was hard for all of us to hear! How did all of this happen so fast? How could this be how my story ends?*

Our lives changed in a matter of hours. The day before, I was excited about getting ready to be in my friend's wedding; today, I'm on a ventilator fighting for my life.

After the initial shock of the news, there were a lot of tears. Everyone, friends and family, came to me individually, shared their special moments, and said goodbye to me before my new journey began. I felt love before but nothing like this. It was so hard to believe I would never see them again or get to tell them how much they meant to me.

God had a different plan for me. My life on Earth as I knew it changed for me, my family, friends, and our community. At 10:45 a.m. on Sunday, November 7, 1993, my new journey began.

# CHAPTER 8

# Yellow Roses

$\mathcal{I}$mmediately after my passing, a representative from the hospital brought my Mom, Dad, Jerry, and Lisa into a private room to talk about what was next. Since I was a young, healthy seventeen-year-old, they spoke to them about donating my organs. This was something I had never really heard about. I mean, I was a teenager. *Why would I?*

The team at LOPA explained how donations save many lives. LOPA, which stands for Louisiana Organ Procurement Association, is a nonprofit organization that started five years before my accident in 1988. Their home office was in Covington, Louisiana, in the southern part of Louisiana, not far from New Orleans. They had representatives in the bigger cities, and we met with the Monroe rep, Laura. She was so kind and loving with my family and explained there would be no charge to them for any of the services.

There was no question about it. My family knew what they wanted to do within minutes, and I was so happy they made that choice. I never thought about it at my age, but that's exactly what I would have done. Organ donation wasn't something that was really taught or brought up. Once the decision was made, my family shared with everyone what was coming next.

As the process began, the hospital kept me on a ventilator for hours to keep blood flowing through my organs until the recipients were notified. Once the families received the call, it wasn't long before the next phase of my life would begin. Each recipient on the list was contacted with the news they had been waiting for while my family grieved their loss. It was so hard for everyone to know I was still in the hospital, and my parents had to wait until surgery was over before they could proceed with my funeral arrangements.

The surgery team removed the organs they could use for those who matched with me. There was not much time for some organs to be in transit. Depending on the organ, it could be a four- to thirty-six-hour window from hospital to hospital. They were even able to use my bones and tissue too. My lungs were the only organs they couldn't use since they were damaged in the accident, and I developed pneumonia from being on the ventilator. The lives of six people were about to change forever.

Wow, I learned so much about organ donation in a short amount of time. The LOPA representative explained the process to my family so everyone had as much knowledge about organ donation as possible. This was the first time anyone we knew had become a donor. She explained how the surgery would go. As promised by the surgical team, no one could tell my organs had been removed since prosthetics were placed where needed for my funeral, and everyone could pay their respects to me and be there for my family.

My parents were not doing well since their baby girl was no longer with them. No parent should ever have to plan their child's funeral. They met with the Kilpatrick Funeral Home to make the arrangements. My brother and sister stepped up to help my parents with the details of my funeral. When the funeral director suggested they put a dress on me, my family didn't agree *at all*. They knew putting a dress on me would not be what I wanted.

Mom picked out my favorite gold silk shirt, wrangler blue jeans, and worn-out Justin cowboy boots. *Yes! That's what I wanted, and Mom knew it.* They gave them my most recent picture so my makeup and hair could look as close to me as possible.

When Lisa arrived at the viewing with just my immediate family, she wasn't happy with what they had done with my hair. I literally looked like I had a helmet on my head. She had to step in and fix my hair because if you have curls, you know you just don't brush curls. Walmart was across the street, so she asked her friends

Mel and Melody to pick up what she needed: an empty water bottle and a can of mousse. They were literally spraying water and adding mousse to bring the curls back so I looked like me. My makeup was all wrong too, so Lisa got her makeup bag and she and Catherine applied my favorite blue eyeshadow, pink blush and light pink lip gloss, making me look like I did a few days earlier.

I laughed at them but was very grateful at the same time. They wanted to make sure everyone remembered me as the curly-haired, fun-loving, blue-eyed girl they so loved. Lisa was very specific that the family spray that was on top of my casket was nothing but yellow roses, the flowers I had loved my whole life.

# CHAPTER 9

# Celebration of Life

**V**isitation was on Monday, November 8, 1993. There were over 500 people in attendance. I didn't realize so many people knew me and my family. It showed how much our family was loved. Even one of the funeral directors said they had never seen a line that long for a visitation. Family from all over the country, Texas, Florida, and Montana, were there, friends I went to elementary school with, church friends, cousins, aunts, uncles, and my grandparents, all of my sibling's close friends. Even some of my teachers from Jack Hayes came to pay their respects. Sabrina and Melanie saw each other and, without saying a word, had the longest hug and lots of tears.

And true to my family's wishes and mine, my casket was covered in the most beautiful family spray of yellow roses. My absolute favorite; they were the flower of friendship which is why I loved them so much.

Some of my favorite songs were chosen; even my all-time favorite, "Purple Rain," played in the background. There were flowers of all shapes, sizes, and colors, and my very favorite, yellow roses were everywhere. So many people knew they were my absolute favorite. Lisa had Jerry get all the photos together for the funeral home so they could put together a slideshow of our favorite family memories and me with my friends. The slideshow was set to loop with many people seeing themselves in the photos from my childhood. It was so special. There were tears and laughter as people remembered the fun times.

Mom and Dad looked like they were in a trance. Mom had a tough time, and everyone worried about her. *Why did this happen to her beautiful baby girl?* I wanted to let her know that I wasn't in pain anymore. The night before my funeral, I went to my Mom in a dream to show her how beautiful Heaven was and assure her I wasn't in pain. I wanted to help relieve just a little bit of her pain and heartbreak if I could. Honestly, I could see the difference in her the next morning; she was still crying but not as hard. She seemed to have a little peace, and I'm so glad I could give her that. She knew that I would always be a part of her.

That night at the funeral home after the visitation would be the last time Mom, Dad, Lisa, Jerry, Rhonda, Meghan, and my grandparents would see me. It was so hard for all of them to say goodbye. I was so grateful for the photo albums and boxes of pictures we had taken throughout the years so my memory could live on.

The morning of the funeral, the sun came up just like a few days ago, but it was very different this time. Today, Tuesday, November 9, 1993, at 10 a.m., my family and friends would say their final goodbyes to me and my life as I knew it. There would be no more sleepovers, bowling tournaments, family reunions, or driving around in my Blazer with the windows down, singing at the top of my lungs.

My funeral was at our Catholic church, Our Lady of Fatima, which was the church we grew up in. There was a full mass after my funeral. My cousins, Brian and Mark, Uncle Robert, Uncle NJ, my cousin Jan's husband, Bill, were all pallbearers. My casket was closed and sat at the front of the church during the service with the beautiful yellow roses on top.

At the end of the service, before everyone was dismissed, they rolled my casket out and placed it in the white hearse in front of the church with cars behind it, ready to carry my immediate family to the cemetery. There was a long line of vehicles in procession to the Memorial Park Cemetery, about a mile from where the accident happened. As the line of cars drove with their headlights on, all vehicles pulled to the side in respect for my family and me. Not sure if all states do that, but we had been taught that in Louisiana.

My final resting place was in the cemetery's Mary Hill Catholic Memorial section, on the far right of the cemetery down a dirt road about halfway down on the left. There was a beautiful oak tree my family used for reference to know they were getting close. My parents had purchased five plots after I was born, hoping we would all be laid to rest together as a family.

There was a small graveside ceremony with some of my close family and friends. They all laid a yellow rose on my casket before it was lowered into the ground. Everyone left for a few hours so they could close the grave. In Louisiana, they don't lower the casket in front of the family. Later the family returns after the burial has taken place to visit the grave. I had no idea how all of this went down. I had never been to a funeral before.

It was hard to see everyone crying so much; I just wanted to tell them I was in Heaven, the most beautiful place I had ever seen, and not in pain anymore. Honestly, I didn't want to go back. I was exactly where I was supposed to be, with God our Father. He had loaned me for a short time, but it was time to be back with Him.

Mom, Dad, Jerry, and Lisa met with the cemetery the next week to design my headstone. Who knew there were so many options: tall, short, big, small. All shapes and sizes. They wanted to do a six-foot flat grey stone, and in the middle would be a huge unicorn with tiny stars around it. At the top left would be music notes, and the top right, my Chevy Blazer etched in stone. My name would be at the very top and the following inscription is below it:

*"Her laughter is still heard, her smile in our memory,*
*God only knows how much we loved you."*
*—Mom, Dad, Lisa, Jerry*

And under the unicorn was this poem:
*God gives us love*
*Something to love lends us*
*So he sent us an angel to visit this green earth and*
*claimed His full bloomed flower before it began to fade.*
*Her mission on Earth fulfilled. God took her home, it was*
*His will. But in our hearts she still lives.*

Wow, such a beautiful tribute to me. There was also a built-in flower vase with my photo on the oval ceramic plate. It was the last school photo I would ever take, and I wore my favorite color-block button-up shirt. It would be several months before my stone was ready. Many people visited and talked to me there to feel close to me, and others spoke to me wherever they were. I heard them all. The first time my family saw the stone, it brought that day back all over again; seeing your last day on earth etched in stone is a tough one.

Mom moved to Tennessee as originally planned and started her new job a few weeks after my funeral. It was heartbreaking that she was beginning this new journey without me. She knew this would be the move that we all needed.

Dad tried to stay busy with work. His life changed completely in a year. He basically lost all three of his girls in different ways. Lisa moved away, he and Mom divorced, and I was in Heaven. Not sure if anyone realized how much this broke him. He was grateful he still had Jerry, Rhonda, and Meghan, and his sisters, nieces, and nephews living there. But eventually, Dad decided he needed a change of scenery, so he moved away to Florida to be near two of his brothers, nieces and nephews, and try to start over again.

As months passed, the numbness was still there. Some days my Mom couldn't get out of bed. Lisa tried her best to be there for her, but it was a pain she couldn't take away. There were many tears and much sadness and anger around my passing. Mom often thought, *Why did this happen to Ret and Andrea? How was Ret's family handling everything? Why were they out all night? What were they doing?* So many things my family didn't understand. There were so many details about the accident my family never knew. So many unanswered questions.

Someone shared a poem with Dad called "God's Child on Loan" by Edgar A. Guest. He went to Kinko's and had bookmark copies made, laminated, and shared with Mom, and they both would keep them on their refrigerators with a unicorn magnet holding it up. He had extra copies made to share with anyone who had lost a child. The poem was so beautiful.

> *"I'll lend to you for a little time*
> *A child of mine," God said*
> *"For you to love while she lives*
> *And to mourn for when she's dead."*

> *"It may be six or seven years*
> *Or twenty-two or three*
> *But will you till I call her back*
> *Take care of her for me?"*

> *"She'll bring her charms to gladden you*
> *And should her stay be brief*
> *You'll have these precious memories*
> *To comfort you through grief."*

*"I cannot promise she will stay*
*Since all from earth return.*
*But there are lessons taught down there*
*I want this child to learn."*

*"I've looked this world over*
*In my search for teachers true*
*In the crowds of this great land*
*I have selected you."*

*"Now will you give her all your love*
*Not think the labor vain*
*Nor hate me when I come to call*
*To take her back again?"*

*It seems to me I heard them say*
*"Dear Lord, thy will be done.*
*For all the joys a child shall bring*
*The risk of grief we'll run."*

*"We'll shelter her with tenderness*
*We'll love her while we may*
*And for the happiness we've known*
*Forever grateful stay."*

*"And should the angels call for her*
*Much sooner than we've planned*

*We'll brave the bitter grief that comes*
*And try to understand."*
— Edgar A. Guest

I knew God had a bigger plan for me because so many things happened later that made sense; at the time, though, it was hard to understand.

*Was it a blessing that my room was already packed?* That was to keep my parents and siblings from having to do it.

*Was it a coincidence that my Mom was moving a few weeks later to start a new job in TN?* She wouldn't have to stay in a home where I wasn't. My parents were divorced, and I think my passing brought them closer together. They drew closer as friends again.

I knew there had to be some positive things from my short time on Earth, but the biggest turned out to be sharing the things I didn't need anymore, my organs.

# CHAPTER 10

# The Gift of Life After Life

There was a list of potential patients who needed a heart, kidneys, corneas, and liver. Individuals are prioritized by medical urgency, waiting list time, and location. As the recipients were found, one by one, their chances to live became greater and greater. Calls were being made all over the state of Louisiana. They received the answers to their prayers with the news they had a chance at a longer life. *Wow! What a sacrifice, but my family knew it was what we all wanted.*

Most of the surgeries took place at around the same time, with some surgeons in the room together, each taking the organ they specialized in. They prayed over me the whole time and also over the ones receiving my organs.

My lungs were not able to be used. Pneumonia was listed on my paperwork following my death because I had been on a ventilator for a while. It wasn't uncommon for that to happen.

I'm glad they were able to use what they could. So many lives and families would change forever after this day and for generations. Once the process started, many factors are included in finding the perfect match. Blood type, tissue type, organ size, and medical urgency were some main factors. Also, how long the recipient had been on the waiting list, and the geographical distance between the donor and the recipient were all considered. If, for some reason, the organ was refused by a transplant team, they would move to the next patient in line that was the best match.

The recipients were from all over Louisiana, so it took a little longer for some to get the organs to the closest hospital to them. Everyone, from the patients to the doctors, treated me and my organs with honor and respect. The recipients didn't know my first name, but they did know a seventeen-year-old healthy female lost her life that day and matched the organ they needed.

There were prayers from all over by perfect strangers to my family for giving their loved ones the ultimate gift of life. They knew someone had to lose someone close to them to save their loved one. I felt famous in a weird way. The word I heard over and over from everyone was Hero. I'd never thought of myself as a Hero, but I was!

Laura, the LOPA representative, explained to my parents that there would be no charge to them for any of this. They were a non-profit that serviced the state's diverse community by supporting families through tragic loss, during the donation process, and along their grief journey. Throughout the entire donation process, I would be treated with the utmost respect and dignity. She also explained that the Traumatic Loss Support Program was designed to guide families through their grief journey and connect them to the resources to help them heal. These services would be something my family could take advantage of whenever needed.

# CHAPTER 11

# I Can See Clearly Now

*L*et me introduce you to Susan. She was a fifty-year-old woman who had always been the most active among her friends; some might even call her hyperactive. She was never one to sit still; when she wasn't working, she volunteered at local food banks.

She was born in Virginia but moved to Louisiana when she was ten. Her parents thought the move would be good for their family. Her Dad had family in south Louisiana, so being close to family was where they needed to be.

There were hard times before the move when some nights her family didn't know where their next meal was coming from. That was where her passion came from for volunteering at food banks when she was older. From her younger years into her teenage years, Susan always wanted to help people. It was in her blood, and she felt like she could make a difference somehow, some way.

She graduated at the top of her class and was in the Honor Society. When she finished high school, she went to Louisiana State University in Baton Rouge to become a nurse. She wanted to take her passion for helping people to a full-time career. After her first four years, she finished with a BSN in nursing and then decided to get a part-time job to go back to become an RN. She chose to specialize in pediatrics, and when she graduated as an RN, she got a full-time job at Ochsner Hospital for Children in New Orleans, one of the top hospitals for children.

Her life felt complete doing something which was always a passion of hers. Susan's family was very small. She had lost her parents a few years ago. Her Mom died of ovarian cancer and her Dad had a pulmonary fibrosis disease. Only she and her older sister, Sandra, were left. They were the best of friends. Susan never married, either. She was married to her career and was totally happy about it. She was changing people's lives every day.

Her career was very challenging. Most days were long, and sometimes she would pull an overnight shift here and there. Although Susan had no children of her own, she was surrounded by many of her friend's kids and two nieces and one nephew. Her patients were also very special to her, almost like having lots of kids. She became close with each patient as well as their parents. She wanted all of them to know that she would be there for them.

In her spare time, running was another of her passions and a way to clear her mind from the day, and became a huge part of her weekly routine. She had been a runner in high school when she joined the track team as an extra-curricular activity and ended up loving it.

On her longer runs, she would take her old Sony Walkman with her favorite cassettes, listen to all the songs on one side, and flip it over for the run back to where she started. It was the perfect amount of time, about thirty minutes on each side.

Her favorite music was '90s hair bands. She loved all those guys with their long hair and makeup. Every Saturday morning, when the sun came up, her neighbors saw her starting her day. It was the time she looked forward to every week, just her and God; it was their time together. These were the runs she would do in silence. She loved her time outside, listening to the birds chirping and just enjoying nature. From every blade of grass to the big oak trees that shaded the path she ran on. There was so much beauty to take in. During the week, she mostly got her runs in at the gym in her apartment complex; that's why Saturdays were so special.

Six months ago, things started to change. The colors of the trees became very dull looking, and the clouds became very blurry. Susan had a hard time focusing on street signs. Driving at night became harder and harder, so she would stay home more or catch a ride with a friend. Then she started noticing that while working at the hospital, she could not see the doctor's notes. This definitely affected her work because of the details that were part of the doctor's orders for every patient. The wrong dosage of medicine could be detrimental to a child.

Wearing her glasses didn't seem to help, so she decided to make an appointment to see her eye doctor. Her optometrist, Dr. Howard, examined her right eye and noticed something that he felt needed to be seen by a specialist. He referred her to Dr. York, an ophthalmologist who was one of the best in the area. Over the next few months and multiple eye tests, she was diagnosed with Fuchs' Dystrophy, which affects the cornea and causes impaired vision and discomfort. Susan's doctor recommended a cornea transplant. *What? Transplant? But I'm only fifty years old?*

After the shock wore off, she met with her doctor to discuss options, and just a few weeks later, he got her added to the Louisiana Organ Transplant waiting list for a cornea with no promise of how long it would be.

Her Saturday runs were no longer possible. She had to take time off work because her condition had worsened. Driving was almost impossible, so she became dependent on her sister, friends, and co-workers to take her everywhere she needed to go. The independence she once knew was gone.

Susan could feel herself slipping into a depressive mental state. All the things she loved, she couldn't do anymore. *What would her purpose be?* Overall, she was pretty positive, but some days she was just mad at God for putting her through this.

One Sunday afternoon at 1:11 p.m. on November 7, 1993, time stood still. The hospital called, letting her know a cornea had become available for her and she must get ready for surgery. *Could this really be happening?* Susan thought it could take months, but God had a different plan.

That's how I was introduced to Susan. She would be the person who received one of my corneas. I heard Susan's prayers, and she prayed for me and my family. As tears ran down her face, she realized she had a second chance to see the blue skies on her weekly runs and the white puffy clouds. She silently thanked my family for making the choice of organ donation. She kept a bag ready to go by the door because she was informed that she needed to always be prepared to go at a moment's notice.

Susan's older sister, Sandra, took her to hospital the next day. It would be an outpatient surgery, so she wouldn't be able to drive home. They arrived at the hospital around 2 p.m., and the team was there waiting for her. This time she was the patient and had to admit; it felt weird being on the other side.

As the doctors and nurses wheeled Susan into the operating room, she was extremely nervous but also very peaceful at the same time. What she didn't know was I was right beside her through this journey. The surgery was a success. It took less than an hour, and Dr. York was pleased with the procedure. He felt it was the best outcome that anyone could have prayed for.

She would wear a patch over her left eye for several weeks as the tissues grew back together. When she was feeling silly, she would say she was a pirate with a patch over her eye. Of course, Susan didn't know that I had a lazy eye when I was six years old, and I wore a patch over my left eye to make my right eye stronger. I would always run around the house telling everyone I was a pirate. So funny how our stories were similar!

A few weeks passed after Susan's surgery, and she noticed that things looked clearer than ever before. Her doctors told her that it could be several weeks or even up to a year before her vision returned to where it should be. She would often talk to me and thank me over and over. I was first on her list during her morning prayers. I wish I could have talked back, but I think she could sense I was there sometimes.

In May of the following year, about six months since the transplant, she slowly restarted her Saturday ritual, deciding to walk for a few weeks before she attempted to run. Her first time running was just a few minutes, which turned into thirty minutes, which turned into an hour, and before long, she was back close to her original time before her vision diminished. On her runs, she would stop and smell the roses, the yellow ones. Every time she was drawn to the yellow ones, she had no idea those were my favorite!

One day she was at the Lakeside Mall and randomly saw someone she knew, and after waving, she realized she didn't know them at all, but I did! It was my fourth-grade teacher, Mrs. Thompson, who had moved to New Orleans to be closer to her family. I was still a part of Susan in many ways; when she realized it, it made her smile every time. It was my way of letting her know I was still around.

She started seeing things like I did, and I thought it was so cool! She saw the beauty in the little things around her. She felt so much love when she looked at life through her renewed vision and was so grateful to me and my family for this blessing. She realized that all of this was to show her a different way of seeing things and that God wasn't punishing her but showing her things differently.

As years passed, Susan told her story and shared about the gift she received from me. She met with the LOPA representative, the same place that organized her transplant, and started volunteering. Susan wanted to raise awareness and the importance of being a registered donor. She spoke at local churches and schools so young adults could understand organ donation's significance and how her life changed forever.

Susan also helped raise money for LOPA by organizing an annual 5k run called The Hero Run. Anyone who was a recipient or connected to one was recognized. This was her way of giving back. After thirty years, I often wonder if she still feels seventeen again some days!

## CHAPTER 12

# Tossing and Turning

Meet Curtis, a fifty-one-year-old black man who worked on a Texas oil rig. Being from Claiborne, Louisiana, on the outskirts of West Monroe, it wasn't uncommon to know someone who worked on a rig or had a family member who did. This was hard work, and many in this line of work were gone a lot but would come home for weeks at a time to be with their families. Curtis had been on a rig since he was twenty-one.

He thought he would go to college on a football scholarship, but an injury to his head would keep him from finishing the season his senior year. The brain injury didn't keep him from working, just playing football in college. He met Beverly their senior year when she transferred from Wossman High School in Monroe.

They dated for the first few years of college until Curtis decided college wasn't for him. Beverly finished and graduated with an accounting degree. She got a great job at a local law firm doing their books.

Curtis wanted to follow in his Dad's footsteps and join the oil rig. It was a great paying job that wasn't the best schedule, but the salary made up for it. At twenty-one, he was going out in the Gulf of Mexico for the first time. This change was hard for Beverly and him, but they made it work.

They decided to tie the knot when they were twenty-two. Curtis had a two-week break, so they got married and had a quick honeymoon to Dallas, Texas which was only about four hours away. Their life was really good for a few years, and they welcomed their son, Curtis Jr., in 1968.

As the years passed, Curtis seemed to be gone more than he was home, and Beverly raised Curtis Jr. almost as a single parent. Unfortunately, their marriage only lasted six years, and they eventually divorced; Jr. lived equal time between his parents. He loved them both and didn't want to live with one full-time. He didn't have a lot of say in the matter, but his parents wanted what was best for him.

He and Beverly stayed friends for the sake of Jr., and she ended up getting remarried a few years later, which Curtis was OK with since he was gone so much.

Jr. would have another male to look after them. Years after the divorce, Curtis let his health go. He never remarried or even dated. All he did was work and sleep.

The weeks when Curtis was home from the rigs, he would have Jr. They would pick back up where they left off. They loved cooking together and going to the movies. Sometimes they would drive to Vicksburg, Mississippi, to visit the Battle of Vicksburg battleground since they both loved history. These two were the best of friends all throughout Jr.'s teenage years and into his early adult years.

But not being healthy all of these years took a toll on Curtis; at forty-five, he was diagnosed with Type 2 diabetes with strict instructions from his doctor to make some lifestyle changes. Being on a boat most of the time made it hard to get the exercise he needed, and while he could have made more healthy food choices, his diet was mostly a lot of processed foods, sugary foods, and the occasional beer, which wasn't great for people with diabetes. He also gained weight which didn't help the diabetes. His doctor stressed the importance of taking care of his health.

On weeks when he was home, and his son stayed with him, Jr. noticed how much Curtis slept. He asked his Dad about it, but Curtis didn't think anything about it; he just thought he was just catching up on the sleep me missed when he was gone. He also noticed that his skin had become very itchy and dry, almost ashy, which he assumed was from the salt water off the coast. Years of living this lifestyle had taken a toll on his overall health. He never really took his diabetes seriously, and it showed.

Every July was his yearly exam and bloodwork. At fifty, he hadn't taken good care of himself, and it was starting to show. His general practitioner, Dr. Adams, ordered a full panel of tests to see if they could pinpoint why he was so tired all the time. The tests came back after a few days, and Curtis' doctor asked that he come to see him in person.

All tests pointed to kidney disease. *Kidney disease?* Curtis was in denial over the diagnosis. Every symptom he had could have been anything else, but after some research, Curtis realized that everything he was experiencing was actually a symptom of kidney disease. His doctor explained that he would eventually need a transplant. *A transplant? I'm only fifty!* It was hard news to hear, but it was a wakeup call.

He was added to the Louisiana Organ Transplant waitlist. There was no promise or guarantee when waiting on an organ; it could be weeks, months, or even years. It must be the perfect match for the transplant to be considered a success. The next time Jr. came over to stay, he told him what was going on with his health and asked that he and his Mom keep him in their prayers.

A month after his diagnosis, he realized he just couldn't work anymore. He took a leave of absence from the rig and was able to spend more time with Jr. He knew he had to get better so he could have more time with his son and the rest of his family. He wanted to see Jr. get married and have children one day. Curtis did what his doctor told him and started changing his eating habits, taking daily walks when he felt up to it. He dropped his extra weight, and Dr. Adams was happy.

Some days were better than others, but he knew God wasn't finished with him. He hadn't always been the praying type, but being at home in this situation had rekindled his relationship with God. And that's where I come in.

It was a chilly November morning, Curtis and Jr. were doing their Saturday ritual of watching cartoons, which they had done together since Jr. was a little boy. *Batman and Robin* was their favorite, but honestly, anything was fine. It was more about the time together. Even at twenty-five, he still enjoyed that time with his Dad.

It had been seven months since the diagnosis, and Curtis' health had gone downhill faster than anyone thought. He barely had an appetite, and when he ate, it usually made him feel sick. He stayed in bed most of the time with extreme fatigue. If he didn't get a kidney soon, he wouldn't be far from death.

That evening on the news, they heard of the story of a car wreck that happened early that morning and ended in two fatalities. They prayed for the families who lost a child. They had no idea that our stories were about to cross paths.

The phone rang at 1:11 p.m. on Sunday, November 7, 1993. Curtis answered and sat there in silence. Tears began to roll down his cheeks as the doctor told him the news; they had a match for his kidney. Curtis had gotten close a few times and wanted to give up, but something inside of him kept pushing. He had a hospital bag ready to go for just that reason.

They got in the car with Jr. driving and headed north. They were about a forty-minute drive from St. Francis Hospital and had been given strict instructions to not be more than two hours away, so they rarely left the house unless Curtis was having a good day, and then they would drive to the park and enjoy the outdoors.

They didn't know much about me except that we were a match and that I was a seventeen-year-old female. He didn't even know my name and never would. He never connected the wreck on the news from the day before with his new kidney.

We met on the day of his kidney transplant when Curtis arrived at the hospital. The team of doctors took him back to prep him for surgery, and Jr. waited in the chapel while Curtis was in surgery.

My right kidney had been removed just a few hours before and was ready to transplant to Curtis. I didn't know they would leave his old kidney and connect mine to his blood vessels so they could start pumping blood through my kidney, which was now his. I was still learning so many things about organ donation. The surgery took about four hours, and everything went as the doctors had hoped. I was right there beside him; he now had my kidney and was doing well.

He went home after five days in the hospital to begin his healing process. It wasn't a fast recovery, but he did everything his doctors told him to do. This time he was taking his health seriously. This was a second chance at a new life; he knew it was a gift and he wouldn't blow it.

Fast forward a few weeks, Curtis recovered as well as his doctors had hoped. He had to meet with the transplant team weekly or sometimes every other week to ensure healing was going as expected. His team told him this would be his routine for a year, and then a once-a-year follow-up if all went well this first year.

Jr. stayed with his Dad for several months after surgery and realized he was doing well enough for him to move out. He bought a little house before his Dad got sick and stayed with him during his recovery.

Then a crazy thing happened through all of this, Jr. had met someone. Marilyn was a young nurse on call for Curtis' home visits right after surgery. She came daily to check on him for the first four weeks. The first time Jr. saw her, he knew she was someone special. They went for coffee at first after she was done checking on Curtis. As weeks turned into months, they spent more and more time together, which made Curtis happy. Six months later, they shared the good news with Curtis that they were getting married.

It reminded Curtis of when he and Bev fell in love long ago. Jr. lit up the same way he used to when looking at Beverly. Curtis was so happy for both of them and knew their marriage would be better than his and Jr.'s Mom. Jr. knew it would be hard for his Dad once he moved out since he had been with him for a while. So, to make the transition a little easier, Jr. got his Dad a small lap dog to keep him company. She was an adorable miniature poodle who wouldn't get any bigger than ten pounds.

*What would he name her?* Curtis had no idea what to call this adorable little puppy. Then one day, he decided that he would name her Coco. Of course, he didn't understand why, but I did. That was the name of my favorite dog we had when I was a child. So, from that day on, Coco was her name. Coco never left his side and would snuggle next to him in his oversized comfy recliner. Sometimes she would even sneak into his bed to lay beside him. He didn't mind at all. He loved that sweet little dog.

Curtis was given his second chance and didn't take that for granted. He lived a long healthy life with the help of my right kidney. He was able to see Jr. get married to Marilyn, be there for the births of their three children, and be a part of their lives.

To keep the tradition going, his grandchildren sometimes spent Friday nights with Curtis. He wanted to have the same Saturday morning tradition of watching cartoons with them, as he did with his son, their dad. Instead of *Batman and Robin*, he now wanted to watch the *Smurfs*, and he wasn't sure why, but I knew.

He also started making Pillsbury cinnamon rolls, and the kids would catch Curtis eating the icing. All of this was because of me. Curtis kept me in his prayers every night for the chance to be with his family longer.

# CHAPTER 13

# Third Times a Charm

Ilona was a fifty-year-old breast cancer survivor when we met. She was a mother of three and had been married to her husband, Wayne, since she was twenty-three. She had a daughter, Kim, from a previous marriage when she was only sixteen. Wayne raised her daughter as his own, and Kim referred to him as Daddy and always would.

She met Wayne through mutual friends in their small Louisiana town of Ruston, fell in love, and married at their tiny church on a Saturday night in April. They started their life together and had their second child, Tracey, about a year later. A little surprise happened five years later, and she became pregnant with their third child, Angie. Their family was sometimes referred to as mixed or blended, but they didn't take offense. Color didn't matter to them; love did.

It was not long after Angie's birth when she was doing her post-pregnancy exams, Ilona's bloodwork came back with some questionable numbers. Her doctor, Dr. Stewart, ordered more extensive tests and discovered Ilona had cervical cancer. She had a full hysterectomy at age thirty and started radiation.

Thankfully the cancer wasn't in an advanced stage which was a blessing since they had caught it early. Ilona was too young to have cancer. Because of her age, she recovered quickly and got back to her regular routine.

Ilona counted her blessings every day and was able to be there for Wayne and their three girls. However, because of the hysterectomy, her hormones went out of control. Her Oncologist, Dr. Owens, started her on hormone patches to balance everything, and she began to feel like she did before her diagnosis.

Six years later, when she was barely thirty-six, she noticed a small lump in her breast. Having checked herself regularly, she knew this was different. Once again, she went back to her doctor's office. This time the news wasn't anything she could have prepared for. After many ultrasounds and scans, Dr. Owens shared with her the news that she had Stage 4 breast cancer; they wanted to do a double mastectomy as soon as possible. Surgery was scheduled three weeks after the diagnosis.

Surgery was successful, but she had to get used to a life without breasts until she could have reconstruction done. A month after the double mastectomy, Ilona started chemotherapy and radiation to help prevent the cancer from returning. It took several months of weekly visits to the hospital before she would be released.

She made many friends during those long hours in the oncology unit at the hospital. Sometimes her girls would go to keep her company and visit with the other patients, many who didn't have family with them. Everyone in the oncology unit became like a small-knit family because of the one thing they had in common, cancer.

A few months later, she finished the treatments and received a clean bill of health. She was cancer free! Her reconstruction surgery was scheduled for the next month, which would get her back to feeling like herself again. She knew she had more of her life ahead, and God had gotten her through this challenging time once again. Life for Ilona was perfect!

Fast forward many years, when Ilona turned forty-nine in the spring of 1992. The kids were growing up so fast. Her daughter, Kim, was thirty-three and had a family of her own. She was married with two kids and lived about thirty minutes away near Monroe. Ilona had family there too, so she could visit when she saw the grandbabies. Ilona loved being a grandmother more than anything! Kim made her a grandmother, years earlier, at forty, making her the only grandmother among her friends.

Her middle daughter, Tracey, turned twenty-six in February and worked at a local law firm in Baton Rouge, Louisiana. She finished LSU law school two years earlier and was happy to be working a job she loved in the career she had dreamed of. Marriage wasn't in her plans, and Ilona and Wayne were OK with that. She was always an independent woman; that's how they raised her.

Her youngest, Angie, was now nineteen. Her baby was now in college at NLU in Monroe, studying to be a schoolteacher. Angie had always loved kids and couldn't wait to start teaching after she graduated. She knew she wanted to be a first-grade teacher and loved the idea of being a part of the early years of a child's life.

Ilona and her husband were now empty nesters, ready to start another chapter of their life together. They decided to move to West Monroe to be closer to two of their girls. It was time to downsize, so they found a one-story home not far from Cheniere Lake.

Wayne took a job at the paper mill so he could work several days on and have several off. He liked having the shift work so they could plan their little getaways. Most of the time, they could be found at the lake fishing in their favorite spot on the bank. They loved being near the water with the stillness until a giant catfish or largemouth bass would get on a line then the excitement began.

After several months of going to the lake, Ilona started noticing that she was getting tired more quickly than she had in her younger years. Her stomach stayed bloated, and she felt nauseated most of the time. She had been through so much, but it felt different this time.

She made an appointment with her general practitioner, Dr. Williams, for yearly bloodwork to check all her levels. What they found was nothing she had ever expected. Her liver was failing.

As she sat in disbelief when he told her, she thought, *Why me?* One more thing she was up against. God being on her side was the only thing she was sure of. Ilona's doctor explained to them how the previous years of radiation when she was thirty, followed by chemotherapy and radiation when she was thirty-six, caused damage to her liver. What saved her life was now the cause of her failing liver.

After a year, her health deteriorated even more, and Dr. Williams said she needed a new liver. Because her previous cancer was never in the liver and the damage was from treatment, not the cancer, she was a candidate for a new liver.

Ilona was added to the Louisiana Organ Transplant wait list at fifty years old. It would be several months of waiting for the call. Every time the phone rang, she got excited hoping it was the call, but most times it was just her girlfriends checking in on her. Then one day, it all changed.

On Sunday afternoon, November 7, 1993, at 1:11 p.m., Ilona received the call she had been waiting for. Tears of joy streamed down her face; she would be receiving a liver, my liver.

This was the day Ilona and I met. Her bag had been packed for months sitting by the door. Luckily Wayne was already off that day, and they got ready to head to St. Francis Hospital. They had no idea that I had just passed there earlier that day. Our families had only been a few hours apart. My family was full of sadness, and her family was full of joy.

Her surgery was scheduled for later that afternoon at 5 p.m. which allowed time for the surgeons to remove mine and prep for her to receive it. We were a perfect match!

She reminded me a lot of my Mom, a strong woman in all aspects of life. Both had been through so much and remained the rock of the family. Her surgery would take close to twelve hours, and then recover in the ICU for a few days. The surgeons were pleased how well the transplant went and informed Wayne that Ilona should return to herself in three to six months.

The surgeons were right; she made a full recovery and bounced back faster than expected. *Was it because she had gotten my seventeen-year-old liver?* Ilona kept me in her prayers daily, thinking about my family often when she saw kids my age at the mall hanging with their friends.

She often wondered what I looked like since my identity was kept private. She just knew I was a seventeen-year-old female. She physically felt my Mom's pain with the loss of her youngest child. Mothers just know.

Ilona noticed some changes after her recovery. When she got her appetite back, the first thing she wanted was chicken spaghetti. *Chicken Spaghetti? I've never had that a day in my life,* Ilona thought. What she didn't know was this was one of Lisa's meals she cooked when Mom would have to work late and one of my favorites. She also started giving her grandkids Tang orange drink and crackers. She had remembered something from her younger years when she visited her Aunt Mary but never really thought about it. That same Mary was the same one that worked at the Little Red School House when I was growing up.

Wayne retired several years later, and they joined a bowling league. Something they had always wanted to do. Their league was at the Western Lanes in West Monroe, but sometimes there would be tournaments at the Bayou Bowl. She noticed the smell of burnt popcorn and pizza when she walked in right away.

She was drawn to a memorial scholarship in my honor that Bayou Bowl had done after I had passed. What was wild was Melanie's little sister, Amy, won the scholarship the first year. Melanie was a little disappointed at first, but then she was really happy that Amy got it. As Ilona was reading about me and the scholarship, she felt a connection to my photo and had no idea that I was the same seventeen-year-old that donated the liver that saved her life.

To everyone's surprise, including Ilona, she was an excellent bowler! Whenever she got a strike, she spun around and took three jumps in the air: my signature move. She had no idea why she did that, but it felt right, and she somehow knew there must have been a connection between us that would always be there. Ilona was grateful for the chance to watch her grandchildren grow up and be a part of their lives.

# CHAPTER 14

# Full Circle

ifty-year-old Willie was a seventh-grade science teacher in Alexandria, Louisiana, called Ellic by the locals which is located almost exactly in the center of the state. He was married to Elaine, the love of his life, for twenty-five years and had two beautiful children, Stacey, eighteen, and Nicholas, Nick for short, twenty-one.

Willie and Elaine met in college at Northeast Louisiana University in Monroe. Willie was an education major with a minor in science. Elaine was a pharmacy major, so she had to take biology classes, and that's where they met.

While growing up, Willie loved everything about science. Usually, you would find him mixing many things together to see if he could make them explode. His parents never knew what concoction they would find in his room. Sometimes they would find leftover food under his bed and wondered if it was an experiment, or he had just forgotten. He had always dreamed of being a scientist ever since he could remember, but as Willie got older, he knew he wanted to be a teacher to share his love of science by teaching others. That was the best of both worlds, doing two things he loved.

After graduation, Willie and Elaine married in the summer and moved to Lafayette. Willie started his new job teaching sixth grade at Arcadia Junior High School in Lafayette, and Elaine, who had finished a degree in pharmacy, got a job as a pharmacist at the local K&B drug store headquartered in New Orleans. They waited a few years after they got married before they had children.

They built a great life in this little Cajun town that was sometimes referred to as the "Happiest City in Louisiana." When their kids were eight and eleven, Willie got a job offer to take a new higher position at Bolton High School in Alexandria, and he couldn't pass it up. He would teach seventh grade and be the head of the science department. Luckily, Elaine could also transfer to the local K&B store in Pineville, which was the next city over. The kids would start at Poland Middle/Junior High School until they were old enough to go to Bolton.

A very active middle-aged man, Willie loved every kind of sport, if it involved a ball. He grew up playing on a local baseball league with some of his best friends in Swartz, on Monroe's outskirts. He played baseball all through high school, and in college, he played on his church baseball team.

As he got older, he wanted to switch things up so he took up tennis. It was a very competitive sport and something he and Elaine could do together. His kids, Stacey and Nick, also loved playing, and often would play a foursome against each other on the weekends. Sometimes it would be boys against girls or parents against the kids. Whichever the case, these were special memories they would always treasure.

Willie loved being a high school science teacher more than anything. He wanted to show his students why he loved it so much, and they were very engaging with him. Willie had his own fashion style, too, and his students would never know which wild shirt he would wear to class that day. He had a vast collection of wild button-up shirts with insects, DNA Molecules, the Periodic Table of Elements, and anything related to science.

Elaine got him a new shirt every Christmas. It had become a tradition for her to see how wild and crazy the next shirt she could find was. She started looking in the summer because you never knew how long it would take from the time you mailed the check with your order and when the shirt would arrive. It was always a waiting game.

In the Summer of 1991, Willie noticed his energy level was declining; he had little to no energy at the end of the day. His legs and feet swelled, especially after playing tennis, which had never happened before.

He knew he wasn't as young as he used to be but considered himself a young man. He also noticed when he showed his students how to dissect a frog, he got confused and forgot what he was saying.

He knew something wasn't right, so he scheduled a visit to his family doctor, Dr. John. After running lots of tests and bloodwork, after several weeks, the diagnosis wasn't what he had anticipated. It was nephrotic syndrome, a type of kidney failure. *What? Kidney Failure?* Willie wasn't prepared for those results, and neither were Elaine and the kids. It came out of nowhere, and they had to navigate what would be next.

Nephrotic syndrome has a group of symptoms that can cause your kidneys to lose their function over time. Willie's urine had become darker and foamy, which he hadn't thought much about. His stomach was bloated most of the time, and he was never hungry, but he had been gaining weight. It all started to make sense, just like a science equation that he would write out for his students to figure out.

Dr. John told Willie and Elaine that he would eventually need a new kidney. Unfortunately, Elaine was not a match as a living donor, so Willie was placed on the Louisiana Organ Transplant waitlist.

A little over two years had passed since Willie's diagnosis, and his health was diminishing by the month. He had two close calls with a donor match, but at the last minute, they fell through. He started on dialysis regularly and constantly prayed for the right match.

His family did their best to keep his spirits up, but Willie was heartbroken when he had to take a leave of absence from school. He just didn't have the energy to teach anymore. He missed his students so much, and they missed him! The teachers who came to fill his spot weren't nearly as fun as Willie and didn't make science exciting anymore.

On November 7, 1993, at 1:11 p.m., Willie received the call he had been waiting for. That's the day we met. Willie would be receiving my left kidney. We were a perfect match!

I was a young and healthy match for Willie. My left kidney was en route in an ambulance from St. Francis Hospital to Alexandria and arrived around the same time as Wille and Elaine. They had arrived at the Rapids Regional Medical Center Alexandria less than two hours after the phone call.

Willie was prepped for surgery which would take about four hours. Little did he know I was right there beside him during the surgery, watching them put my left kidney into his body. The team of surgeons connected the new kidney to his blood vessels and bladder. The surgery was a success. Dr. John came out to tell Elaine, Stacey, and Nick, that the surgery couldn't have gone any better.

Even though there was a chance the kidney wouldn't work immediately, he beat all odds, and my kidney started working instantaneously. He recovered for several days in the hospital, getting up every few hours to walk around. His students sent balloons, cards, and letters wishing him well. He was finally on the road to recovery and ready to start the next phase of his life.

Willie went home after about a week in the hospital. Dr. John wanted to ensure there was no infection, my kidney functioned and was accepted by his body. Willie recovered at home, and his daughter, Stacey, went to Blockbuster and rented tons of movies to watch during the weeks he would be at home. Of course, she picked many of her favorites, and they would sometimes watch them together. Willie watched all the movies the first week; the one he watched over and over was *Dirty Dancing*. He had no idea this was my all-time favorite movie and one I had watched with Melanie religiously over and over when we were kids.

He returned to his students in the spring of 1994; to his student's surprise, he wasn't wearing his wild science shirts anymore. During his recovery at home for the past few months, he went through all his childhood and teenage stuff and came across all his rock t-shirts and got them all washed. He was surprised they didn't fall apart so he decided to start wearing them instead of his wacky shirts and was really excited they still fit.

He also started craving Twinkies and chocolate milk, so he would go to the canteen on breaks and get them every day. That was a new one for him. He wondered if it must have been my favorite after-school snack since he never liked them before. Willie smiled knowing that somewhere deep down, a part of me was still living through a part of him.

Several years later, Willie was back in Monroe visiting his family and recognized someone he played baseball with growing up. It had been over forty-two years since they had seen each other, so it took them a few minutes to recognize each other, yet it was also very familiar—like family. Nathan and Willie decided to catch up over dinner at Johnny's Pizza to fill each other in on all that had happened since they last saw each other. *Remember my favorite pizza place?*

Nathan's eyes filled with tears as Willie told him about his kidney transplant At the time, Willie didn't know Nathan was my Uncle NJ, and they were at the Johnny's location about five miles from where the wreck happened. NJ told Willie all about me and things made sense for Willie. He knew he felt a little different after surgery but had no idea that some of the new stuff he now enjoyed were my favorite things.

This was a full circle moment for all of us! Willie retired from teaching several years after his transplant. He was ready to start the next chapter of his life with

Elaine, Stacey, her husband Todd, Nick and his wife, Sarah, and their five grandchildren. Our story would be told often, and my family and I were always in their prayers.

# CHAPTER 15

# Flying the Friendly Skies

The day I met Michael, he was in the hospital room waiting for surgery to replace his left cornea. Michael was a thirty-year-old bachelor who traveled weekly with his job as a Delta Airlines pilot for almost ten years; it was his passion and his life. He traveled all over the world but always loved coming home to Louisiana. He was born and raised there and knew he would always call it home. Michael grew up on the north side of Monroe, not too far from where we did, and ended up moving to West Monroe in junior high. He was the only boy in the middle of his two sisters.

Michael was considered a "party boy" among his friends and never really took things too seriously; he was always the life of the party with an infectious smile. He was the star football player, homecoming king, and an all-around great guy with sandy blonde hair and piercing blue eyes.

Michael never really dated much except for a few years when he and his high school sweetheart, Cindy, were together. But they had different thoughts for their future; she wanted to get married and start a family, and Michael didn't. They didn't stay together after college since he always knew that he wanted to be a pilot, so settling down wasn't in his plan.

He graduated from NLU with a bachelor's degree in aviation and worked at the Monroe Regional Airport so he could be around flying all day. In his spare time, he enrolled in flight school. There were several levels to get through for his commercial license. Michael planned on following in his family's footsteps since his Dad, Tom, had flown earlier in his life but he decided to take a desk job and worked at the Delta Headquarters based in Monroe at the time. His grandfather, Dwayne, had been a crop duster his whole life and took Michael flying when he was young. Michael had always been surrounded by the world of flying.

After putting in many flying hours and flight school, Michael flew commercially for Delta Air Lines at twenty-two years old and knew his life was exactly where it should be.

On a flight back into Monroe in the spring of 1993, he noticed he had trouble seeing the dials on the plane's control panel. Michael wore glasses for distance, but noticed they weren't helping at all anymore. Daytime flights became almost impossible, even with his sunglasses on. His left eye was so sensitive to the light he could barely stand it, and it felt like he had sand in it all the time. It stayed red most of the time. Eye drops would soothe if briefly, but overall, he was in constant pain.

After several visits to the eye doctor, and many rounds of antibiotics that didn't work, they concluded that Michael had a parasite in his eye, and over the years, it caused scarring which impaired his vision. It was a condition called Keratitis. *How would he be able to continue flying?* The one thing he loved more than anything. The doctor explained that this was caused by a scratch to his eye. He shared the diagnosis with his parents and the memory of the incident came back to him.

When he was in high school, they were at Moon Lake one weekend and decided to make a bonfire right before sunset at the end of the day. Michael volunteered to gather wood, grabbing dead branches from the trees near the bank. He pulled on one branch, which broke and scratched his left eye. It hurt when it happened, but he didn't think anything else about it and continued to swim in the bayou water for weeks after that happened.

Little did he know, the tree branch scratch created a fungal infection in his eye, and the bayou water had parasites in it which damaged his eye gradually over the years. He would keep eye drops on hand because he always thought it was his allergies but year by year it got worse.

He met with Dr. Jones, an ophthalmologist in Monroe, who explained the damage to his cornea and that the only treatment would be a transplant. *Wait! What, a transplant?*, he thought. Michael sat in Dr. Jones' office in complete shock. It didn't seem as scary as he explained how the procedure worked. The surgery itself wouldn't be painful. There would be some discomfort after and some adjustments to his daily routine.

Michael was added to the Louisiana Organ Transplant waitlist. At thirty years old, Michael would be having a cornea transplant to get his 20/20 vision back. There was no guarantee on how long it would take to get the call. It could be days, weeks, or even months. Michael called his parents to explain the procedure, and his Mom added him to their church's prayer list, hoping to have a donor sooner than later. It also meant someone had to pass away for him to receive it so she also prayed for the family who would be going through a loss.

He received the call about my cornea on Sunday, November 7th, at 1:11 p.m. He immediately called his parents, excited to let them know the good news. He needed them to drive him to the hospital the next day. His surgery was scheduled for the next morning at St.

Francis Hospital, the same hospital where I had passed a few hours before.

Michael actually lived in West Monroe, so he didn't have far to travel. He lived across the river from St. Frances Hospital, about twenty minutes away. We were a perfect match! Michael had no idea that the same day of his surgery was the same day my family was getting ready for my visitation.

Though my name was kept private, Michael knew of a family in town going through one of the most difficult times of their lives after losing their daughter. All he knew about me was that I was a young healthy seventeen-year-old female from Louisiana. He didn't even know we were from the same town. No one realized that Michael's older sister, Cathy was my second-grade teacher at Jack Hayes. She attended my visitation later that evening. No one ever connected the stories. But I knew.

The surgery was a success. Recovery took several weeks, so Michael took some personal time off from Delta to recover completely. His Mom would bring some of his favorite meals, like her homemade red beans and rice with cornbread, country fried steak with mashed potatoes, green beans, banana pudding, and pecan pie, to name a few. He could get used to this. His pantry stayed pretty bare, and his refrigerator had some expired milk and a half bottle of ketchup, and that was it. Since he traveled so much, he would just grab something on the way home from the airport for dinner.

During his recovery, he couldn't read well because he had to wear a patch over his eye for a few days, reminding me of the pirate story and my patch. He spent this time at home reminiscing and thinking about his life and the path he had chosen. He loved his career, but he was lonely. He missed not having someone to come home to after a long week of travel. He missed not having kids and was grateful for his nieces and nephews.

He took out a box from his attic with his high school yearbooks and pictures from prom and came across a picture of Cindy. *Where was she now? Was she married? How many kids did she have?* he wondered. He pulled out his collection of CDs from a storage case that was a 3-ring binder with plastic sheets that held four CDs on each side in little clear pockets. He had a varied collection of Rock, Country, and Pop. Flipping through, he came across the *Purple Rain* Soundtrack, which was my very favorite, and the favorite of his ex-girlfriend, Cindy. He wasn't sure why he still had that CD but loved listening to it for the first time in years. It brought back so many memories that he cherished.

After eight weeks, Michael could drive again on his own and eventually get back to flying within a few months. He missed his days in the open sky, which he saw differently now with an appreciation for the little things and the beauty all around him.

Years later after Michael's surgery, Lisa flew back to Louisiana in the fall of 1997, for her ten-year class reunion. She usually drove, but this time she needed to get in and out because she was working for two country artists, Rhett Akins and Charlie Daniels. Delta was the only airline that flew into Monroe from Nashville. She called the airline and booked her flight leaving Nashville on a Thursday morning so she would have time to visit family before the reunion started.

That day, as she was boarding the flight with a connection in Atlanta, Georgia, Michael was piloting the particular flight to Monroe. He stood outside the cockpit greeting everyone as he always did, but that day, as the passengers boarded the plane, he and Lisa locked eyes. This connection felt different than the others; there was an interesting energy neither could explain. They both got chills and stared at each other for several seconds like they had known each other their entire lives. In a weird way, they both knew something was special but didn't know why. I was grateful that I got to see my big sister one more time.

Michael met the woman who would become his wife at thirty-five years old. Her name was Michelle (my middle name), and they met at North Monroe Baptist Church, the church Michael and his family attended when he was younger. He started attending again and met her when his younger sister Stephanie had introduced them. They taught Sunday school together, and Michelle had unfortunately lost her first husband to cancer a few years back.

Michelle was a hairdresser, had her own shop in Monroe, and owned a home near the church in a neighborhood called Treasure Island. *Wow really? Treasure Island? Michelle had grown up in the neighborhood and lived there the same time we did.* She knew when she got older, she wanted to stay there. Her family lived a few streets over from us on Spyglass Drive. It was toward the back of the island, but she knew she always wanted a house on the bayou. She and her first husband bought a house on Silver Drive when they got married.

After he passed, she didn't date and never really thought about it until the day she met Michael at church. She and Michael fell in love, and he asked her to marry him shortly after that. They were ready to start their new life together.

Michael sold his house in West Monroe and moved across the river back to Monroe, his old stomping ground. Everything in life felt right. They never had children, but they had two dogs who felt like their babies. They started their life together in a house they bought on Fortune Drive on the bayou with a beautiful dock out back.

He and Michelle would get up every morning when he was home with a fresh cup of Community Coffee and sit on their dock, watching the sunrise and counting all their blessings. *Coincidence? I don't think so. All of this was part of God's plan.*

# CHAPTER 16

# One Heart Can Change the World

**S**amuel and I met late on a Sunday afternoon in November when he showed up at the Our Lady of the Lakes Medical Center for his heart transplant. This wasn't the first time he had been at this hospital. Ten years prior, at forty-one, Samuel had his first heart attack and was diagnosed with coronary artery disease (CAD), which is a condition that affects the arteries that supply blood to your heart. He always had the symptoms but never connected them with his heart. His neck and back stayed tense, and he sometimes suffered numbness in his hands. He really didn't pay much attention to it because he was in a high-stress job as an attorney.

Samuel had followed his father's and grandfather's footsteps and practiced criminal law. Their family founded one of the biggest firms in Baton Rouge, Louisiana and represented high-profile trials. Samuel was on the news frequently regarding a big trial and had the reputation of being a bulldog attorney. Law was his life.

While growing up, Samuel loved watching *Perry Mason* with his grandfather when he would spend weekends with his grandparents. He knew that's what he wanted to do! He attended Law School at LSU and graduated at the top of his class. He met Patricia, and it was love at first sight while they were in college. They married a year after graduation and started a family right away. Samuel and Patricia had two children, twins, a son, Joseph, and a daughter, Jamie.

Samuel felt the pressure of keeping the family tradition with the law firm; most days he worked fourteen hours or more. His entire staff of employees could barely stand to be in the same room with him. He would scream daily at his secretary and some days made her cry. He was always stressed out, and when he tried to unwind, he couldn't; he just couldn't turn it off.

He and Patricia had a wonderful life together when he was around. They didn't fight much, but he made many promises that, at the last minute, he would miss or have to cancel, and that caused a strain on the marriage.

The kids started noticing their Dad wasn't around much which, led to resentment on their part. Missed ballgames, recitals, birthday parties, and even a kindergarten and middle school graduation; the kids felt like they were raised in a single-parent household.

Patricia worked as a secretary at the school, so she could be on the same schedule as the kids, which made things not seem as bad as they were. The kids grew up, and their Dad wasn't there to see it. As they got older, their relationship with him was disconnected.

Samuel had a massive heart attack at forty-one years old and ended up in the hospital. The doctors explained to him that he had coronary artery disease. This scared him enough to take measures to remove some of the stress at his firm. Being a diabetic didn't help his health situation either. As much as he tried to take things off his plate, no one did what he needed in the way he wanted it done. So, he just did it himself. Patricia tried her best to remind him that he had people to help him who he was paying, but he was so stubborn he insisted that his way was the only way to get things done.

Samuel did better for several years, being present at graduations and taking the kids to college, but his old ways eventually crept back in. High-stress cases came in and he couldn't pass them to his partners. He wanted to be in control.

Nine years after his first diagnosis of CAD, he had his yearly checkup with his heart doctor, and unfortunately, the news was nothing he was ready for. His doctor informed him that the CAD had worsened, and he would need a heart transplant.

He couldn't believe what he had just heard. He was only forty-nine years old. Patricia was at a loss for words. She thought he was doing better but the stress of his job was too much for his health. Dr. Nelson, his heart specialist, explained to Samuel that his prognosis wouldn't be good if he didn't get a heart in the next year.

That day his name was added to the Louisiana Organ Transplant waitlist. Unfortunately, he knew that if he didn't get a new heart, he wouldn't live to see his kids have kids. Samuel kept a bag packed in the sunroom by the back door. It sat there for months, not knowing if he would ever have the chance to use it. One Saturday in November, everything changed.

On November 7, 1993, at 1:11 p.m., Samuel received a call that changed his life forever. His perfect match was found. He and Patricia sat crying for joy and praying for the family that had just lost their seventeen-year-old daughter. As parents, they couldn't imagine how the parents were dealing with this tragedy.

Dr. Nelson explained the timeliness of this procedure, so he and Patricia headed to New Orleans for his heart transplant. Patricia called Joseph and Jamie to let them know about the surgery.

Shortly after 5 p.m., they headed to New Orleans. At the same time they were driving to the hospital, I was in the operating room, being stitched back up after my organs were removed by each surgeon. Timing was everything when it came to the heart. There was roughly a four-to-six-hour window from the time my heart was removed to the time it could enter Samuel's body.

His surgery took about three hours to complete. The surgeons were very pleased with the procedure. As they were closing his chest cavity, they watched as my heart began to beat in Samuel's chest. I prayed he would feel the love I had in my heart, the love I had for my family and friends, the love I had for the little things in life, and the love I had for music. Samuel didn't know it, but I was right there with him the whole time. Dr. Nelson explained his recovery could take anywhere from three to six months.

For once in Samuel's life, he had no choice but to slow down. Sometimes things that seem like bad things happening to us can be a huge blessing in disguise. He took time off from the firm to fully recover, and during those months, Samuel started reading more than he had in years. He picked up one of his all-time favorites from childhood, *Treasure Island*. It had a different meaning now reading it as an adult. It wasn't just about finding gold; it was about greed too. The most satisfaction should come from developing wisdom, integrity, and self-knowledge. *Whoa! This sounded like his life.*

His daughter Jamie came to stay with her parents during his recovery and enjoyed being back at home for a while. Joseph was also following in the family business as a lawyer and was working at the family firm, keeping things going while his Dad was recovering. Samuel felt comfortable leaving him in charge. He was a great lawyer and a lot calmer than he ever was.

Jamie was enjoying this time together with her Dad too. She had a membership at the new Blockbuster video store in town, so she rented lots of movies on VHS. One day she came home with *Groundhog Day*, which had come out earlier that year. Samuel had to be careful not to laugh too hard because of his incision.

In reality, it was funny and also a little sad for him. The movie felt like his life in so many ways. He realized that he had been living like the weatherman Phil Connors played by Bill Murray, who was stuck in a spinning hamster wheel, not going anywhere, living the same day over and over until his character began changing things to hopefully not repeat the same day again. Every day, he was stuck in the same day with the choice to make things different.

As crazy as it sounds, this movie changed everything for Samuel. He knew he had been given a second chance at life and wouldn't mess it up this time. Patricia would catch him looking through their family photo albums with many photos without him in them. He would have tears of regret in his eyes for the years he lost with his family.

He and Joseph would talk about the things he missed, and Joseph shared how it felt without him being there during many crucial years. *For what? Gold?* He may have had lots of money in the bank, but was empty inside.

This time around, things would be different. God had given him this second chance to make things right for his family. He started every morning before getting out of bed by holding his chest and feeling my heart beat, saying a prayer for me, grateful for this second chance. Samuel smiled more, laughed often, and loved harder. Even his kids wondered what was happening with their Dad asking him if he was OK.

One day he and Jamie were at the mall, and he passed a store window with a Unicorn figurine displayed. Samuel had to have it but he wasn't sure why. He often wondered if some things he felt differently were because of me. He knew nothing about me except that I was a seventeen-year-old female. This experience literally changed Samuel for the rest of his life. It literally changed Samuel for the better.

About six months after his surgery, he decided to go back to work. But this time, things were different. During his time off, Samuel realized what he was doing was something that his family had always done, but really wasn't what he wanted to do. He wanted to practice law, but this time around, he would be working with individuals planning their estate. Joseph now ran the family firm and was in charge so Samuel could stay in the office practicing estate law as his specialty. The firm was a peaceful place for everyone, and his employees were grateful for his literal change of heart.

Samuel had a small office at the end of the hall, much smaller than the one he gave to Joseph. Some days you could hear him blaring "Welcome to the Jungle" by Guns N' Roses to get the weekend started, which he sang at the top of his lungs. The unicorn figurine sat on his desk every day, and when anyone asked about it, he was able to explain it was his way of sharing his story of receiving a new heart, my heart.

He encouraged his clients to become organ donors as part of their estate planning because he wouldn't be alive today if someone hadn't done it for him. Because of my family and me, Samuel could keep living the beautiful life he had always dreamed of. This time around, it was much different, and Samuel was present physically and emotionally. He was now at all of the holiday functions, births of his grandchildren, birthday parties, and even his retirement party.

Samuel and his family kept me in their prayers every night before bed, thanking me for the extended years he had with his wife, children, and grandchildren. Samuel spent time with his grandchildren that he never had with his children. Yes, he had regrets, but the twins were grateful for his time with their kids.

The unicorn figurine sat on the shelf in the living room long after Samuel retired, and his grandkids also knew the story behind it. After this experience, the family motto became, "One heart can change the world."

# CHAPTER 17

# Did you know?

1. Every donor can save up to eight lives and enhance over seventy-five more lives through donating organs, bones, skin, valves, Saphenous vein, ligaments, and corneas.

2. Many organ transplant recipients describe a change in personality, reporting they have acquired the tastes, emotions, and even memories of their deceased donors.

3. As of March 2022, there are currently over 106,000 people on the national transplant waiting list. The list is diverse, including people of every age, ethnicity, and gender.

4. In 2022, over 42,800 transplants were performed.

5. In 2022, the US reached a historic milestone, achieving its 1 millionth organ transplant, more than any other country worldwide.

6. There is no cost to the donor's family or estate for organ and tissue donation.

7. Every ten minutes, someone is added to the organ transplant waiting list.

8. The kidney is the most commonly transplanted organ.

9.  You can donate one kidney or a lobe of your liver while you're still living. Most living donations happen between family members or close friends. However, others choose to be living donors for someone they don't know, known as a non-directed or altruistic donation. Nearly 6,000 living donations take place each year.

10. As of 2022, 170 million people in the U.S. have registered as donors.

11. Organ recipients are often 50+ years old.

12. Hearts and lungs must be transplanted within approximately four hours after being removed from the donor. Livers can be preserved 8-12 hours; a pancreas can be preserved for 8-12 hours; intestines can be preserved for approximately 8 hours; kidneys can be preserved for 24-36 hours.

13. The brain is the only organ that cannot be transplanted.

14. A common myth is that the ER won't save you if they know you are an organ donor. The ER does not know if you are an organ donor or not until after death.

15. Also, more than 25,000 kidney transplants were performed in the United States for the first year ever in 2022.

16. You can register to be an organ donor on the heart app on your iPhone, and no one has to know.

17. In Louisiana, you can register on LA Wallet, where you have your driver's license or any other licenses listed.

# Author's Note

This story is based on the facts about Andrea's life and death. The story was written twenty-nine years after her passing and written in Andrea's voice and perspective by her sister, Lisa.

In 2021, with the help of Libbie Harrison at LOPA in Covington, Louisiana, Lisa found out the first names of each recipient and the organ they received. This information inspired her to share Andrea's story, but not knowing more about the recipients, the story became Lisa's vision of who they were and how their lives changed.

With the help of Jerry, her friends, family, and Andrea's friends, Lisa brought Andrea to life through personal stories and memories. Unfortunately, Lisa and Jerry lost their Mom and Dad many years before she could share the book with them. Writing this story brought healing to Lisa, who had not been able to process Andrea's death when she passed.

Through the years, Lisa always wondered if, after they received Andrea's organs, the recipients' felt different. Their stories are fictional because Lisa only had their first names and ages. There were no computer files, just a spreadsheet with Andrea's name, age, and death date with a list of names and the organs they received.

She released this book thirty years after Andrea's passing on August 10, 2023, on what would have been Andrea's forty-seventh birthday. Andrea's Hero story will hopefully inspire and educate those who don't know much about organ donation and remind people to be kind, have hope, and love hard.

Andrea's life was short, but her memory lives on. Lisa's hope with this book is to remind you that one selfless act creates endless ripples, which is LOPA's motto.

We are never gone if someone says our name . . .

# Author Bio

Louisiana, turned Nashville native, Lisa Boullt has just embarked on her twenty-sixth year in the Music Business. She works with some of Nashville's biggest songwriters/artists, who are also some of her best friends. It's a perfect combination! Lisa's background in music made her realize the importance of how words and sharing a story can change people's lives.

This book resulted from Lisa's grieving process of her sister, who passed in 1993. She was inspired to write Andrea's story from her point of view, share the recipient's fictitious stories, and bring awareness of Organ Donation to young adults.

Lisa resides in Nashville, Tennessee, with her better half, Mike, and their three fur babies. Lisa goes to church at World Outreach in Murfreesboro, Tennessee, and in her spare time, she volunteers with Faithfully Restored and is a producer on the *Good Grief Good God* podcast.

Instagram: @lisaboullt_17again
Facebook: @LisaBoullt17Again
lisaboullt.com

# Acknowledgements

I am grateful to God for putting this story in my heart and guiding me through this and for everyone that helped me along this journey of healing. I couldn't have done it without you.

Mike, thank you for always encouraging me to follow my heart. I love you.

Lots of love to all my friends, Andrea's friends, family, and my brother Jerry, who would answer the most random questions about when we were kids every time I called. Thank you for sharing your favorite memories of Andrea with me.

Also, thank you to JuLee Brand at W. Brand Publishing for reminding me words matter and assisting me in sharing Andrea's story.

For the ones that never had a chance to know Andrea, I hope this story will give you an idea of who she was. To us she was our funny, wild, 17-year-old and to others she became a Hero.

*Our Family in 1991*

*Andrea, Jerry, Mom,Dad, Lisa*

*Andrea Michelle Boullt*

*August 10, 1976–November 7, 1993*

This is a drawing of the tattoo I got December of 2021. This tattoo represents the beginning of this journey for me. After receiving a coin from LOPA with their logo, I was inspired to come up with my version of their message, which is, "One selfless act creates endless ripples."

My tattoo Artist, Mike Kepper, and I came up with this design together. To me it represents the ripple effect of spreading love and kindness.

Printed in the USA
CPSIA information can be obtained
at www.ICGtesting.com
LVHW040718030823
754038LV00025B/126